WHSmith

Challenge

Maths

KS2: Year 6 Age 10–11
Paul Broadbent and
Peter Patilla

Hachette UK's policy is to use papers that are natural, renewable and recyclable products and made from wood grown in sustainable forests. The logging and manufacturing processes are expected to conform to the environmental regulations of the country of origin.

Orders: please contact Bookpoint Ltd, 130 Milton Park, Abingdon, Oxon OX14 4SB. Telephone: +44 (0)1235 827720. Fax: +44 (0)1235 400454. Lines are open 9.00a.m.–5.00p.m., Monday to Saturday, with a 24-hour message answering service. Visit our website at www.hoddereducation.co.uk.

© Paul Broadbent and Peter Patilla 2013
First published in 2007 exclusively for WHSmith by Hodder Education
An Hachette UK Company
338 Euston Road
London NW1 3BH

This second edition first published in 2013 exclusively for WHSmith by Hodder Education
Teacher's tips © Matt Koster 2013
Impression number   10 9 8 7 6 5 4 3 2
Year   2018 2017 2016 2015 2014 2013

Cover illustration by Oxford Designers and Illustrators Ltd
Illustrations © Hodder Education
Typeset in Folio Book 14pt by DC Graphic Design Ltd
Printed in Italy

A catalogue record for this title is available from the British Library

ISBN 978 1444 188 431

Conten

How this book can help your child

- This book has been written for children who are between 10 and 11 years old.

- It will support and improve the work they are doing at school, whichever Maths scheme they use.

- The activities in the book have been carefully written to include the content expected of children at this stage in their development.

- The activities will help prepare your child for all types of tests.

Materials needed

- Pencil, eraser, watch and centimetre ruler.

Using this book

- There are 24 topics and 4 tests in the book. Each test covers 6 topics.

- Each topic is about a week's work.

- Do give help and encouragement. Completing the activities should be fun!

- A calculator should not be used for work in this book.

- Do let your child mark his or her own work under your supervision and correct any careless mistakes he or she might have made.

- When all the tests have been completed let your child fill in the Certificate of Achievement on the opposite page

- Each double page has a title, explanation of the learning point, practice section, and challenge section.

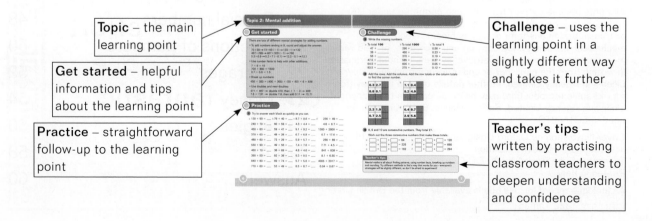

Topic – the main learning point

Get started – helpful information and tips about the learning point

Practice – straightforward follow-up to the learning point

Challenge – uses the learning point in a slightly different way and takes it further

Teacher's tips – written by practising classroom teachers to deepen understanding and confidence

This certifies that

_____

has completed

CHALLENGE ENGLISH YEAR 6

on _____

Scoring _____ on TEST 1

_____ on TEST 2

_____ on TEST 3

and _____ on TEST 4

Total score out of 100 _____

40–49	good effort
50–59	well done
60–69	fantastic
70–100	brilliant

Topic 1: Place value – decimals

Get started

A decimal point separates whole numbers from decimal fractions.

6·257

units (6 units)   tenths ($\frac{2}{10}$)   hundredths ($\frac{5}{100}$)   thousandths ($\frac{7}{1000}$)

To multiply by 10:	To multiply by 100:
move the digits one place to the left	move the digits two places to the left
$6.53 \times 10 = 65.3$	$6.53 \times 100 = 653$

To divide by 10:	To divide by 100:
move the digits one place to the right	move the digits two places to the right
$89.5 \div 10 = 8.95$	$89.5 \div 100 = 0.895$

A zero on the end of a decimal doesn't change its value. $1.6 = 1.60 = 1.600$

Practice

1 Write the value of the bold digit in each of these.

a 3.**6**5 ____   b 18.3**4** ____   c **1**2.06 ____   d 0.14**5** ____   e 365.**1** ____

f 8.9**9**1 ____   g 0.0**7** ____   h 14.61**8** ____   i 3.**6**02 ____   j 12.03**9** ____

2 Write these fractions as decimals.

a $\frac{4}{10}$ _____   b $\frac{7}{10}$ _____   c $\frac{5}{10}$ _____   d $\frac{3}{10}$ _____   e $\frac{9}{10}$ _____

f $\frac{45}{100}$ _____   g $\frac{64}{100}$ _____   h $\frac{92}{100}$ _____   i $\frac{8}{100}$ _____   j $\frac{14}{100}$ _____

k $\frac{755}{1000}$ _____   l $\frac{250}{1000}$ _____   m $\frac{399}{1000}$ _____   n $\frac{925}{1000}$ _____   o $\frac{78}{1000}$ _____

Teacher's tips

Numbers are sometimes written to 'one decimal place' (tenths) or 'two decimal places' (hundredths). This is different from moving digits by a 'place' to multiply or divide by 10, or two places to multiply or divide by 100.

Challenge

3 Write the answers.

a   × 10   b × 100   c ÷ 10   d ÷ 100

7.2 → _____	6.15 → _____	12.1 → _____	14.6 → _____
16.3 → _____	3.8 → _____	14.8 → _____	30 → _____
0.45 → _____	2.77 → _____	7.6 → _____	89.3 → _____
1.033 → _____	0.051 → _____	0.35 → _____	6.5 → _____
0.805 → _____	1.203 → _____	9.01 → _____	0.8 → _____

4 Write the decimals shown on these number lines.

a

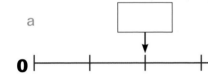

b

c

d

5 Rearrange each set of digits to make the number nearest to 1.

a   8 0 2 1   b   3 5 0 2   c   6 9 0 3   d   5 8 1 1

_ . _ _ _   _ . _ _ _   _ . _ _ _   _ . _ _ _

Topic 2: Mental addition

Get started

There are lots of different mental strategies for adding numbers.

- To add numbers ending in 9, round and adjust the answer:

  $73+59 \rightarrow 73+60 \ (-1) \rightarrow 133-1 \rightarrow 132$
  $467+299 \rightarrow 467+300 \ (-1) \rightarrow 766$
  $5.2+6.9 \rightarrow 5.2+7 \ (-0.1) \rightarrow 12.2-0.1 \rightarrow 12.1$

- Use number facts to help with other additions:

  $7 + 8 = 15$
  $700 + 800 = 1500$
  $0.7 + 0.8 = 1.5$

- Break up numbers:

  $456 + 380 = (400 + 300) + (50 + 80) + 6 = 836$

- Use doubles and near-doubles:

  $471 + 467 \rightarrow$ double 470, then $+ 1 - 3 \rightarrow 938$
  $7.8 + 7.91 \rightarrow$ double 7.8, then add 0.11 $\rightarrow 15.71$

Practice

1 Try to answer each block as quickly as you can.

a	b	c	d
130 + 90 = ___	79 + 40 = ___	8.7 + 8.6 = ___	236 + 49 = ___
240 + 70 = ___	60 + 59 = ___	4.3 + 4.4 = ___	4.8 + 6.7 = ___
450 + 80 = ___	59 + 47 = ___	9.1 + 9.2 = ___	1300 + 2800 = ___
370 + 60 = ___	49 + 28 = ___	6.7 + 6.8 = ___	0.7 + 17.6 = ___
480 + 80 = ___	72 + 29 = ___	5.9 + 5.7 = ___	256 + 69 = ___
550 + 90 = ___	49 + 56 = ___	7.4 + 7.6 = ___	7.71 + 4.5 = ___
460 + 70 = ___	38 + 69 = ___	4.8 + 4.6 = ___	841 + 839 = ___
390 + 50 = ___	82 + 39 = ___	9.3 + 9.5 = ___	8.1 + 6.55 = ___
840 + 80 = ___	69 + 74 = ___	5.7 + 5.6 = ___	4005 + 2017 = ___
770 + 60 = ___	53 + 49 = ___	8.5 + 8.7 = ___	0.04 + 0.67 = ___

Challenge

2 Write the missing numbers.

a To total **100**

47 + _____

38 + _____

56 + _____

47.5 + _____

64.5 + _____

83.5 + _____

b To total **1000**

290 + _____

460 + _____

370 + _____

585 + _____

605 + _____

275 + _____

c To total **1**

0.56 + _____

0.23 + _____

0.19 + _____

0.37 + _____

0.05 + _____

0.12 + _____

3 Add the rows. Add the columns. Add the row totals or the column totals to find the corner number.

a

6.3	2.7	
8.8	0.1	

b

7.1	0.4	
8.2	4.9	

c

2.3	1.9	
0.7	2.5	

d

6.4	8.7	
2.9	5.6	

4 8, 9 and 10 are consecutive numbers. They total 27.

Work out the three consecutive numbers that make these totals.

a ☐ + ☐ + ☐ = 84

b ☐ + ☐ + ☐ = 120

c ☐ + ☐ + ☐ = 225

d ☐ + ☐ + ☐ = 660

e ☐ + ☐ + ☐ = 162

f ☐ + ☐ + ☐ = 294

Teacher's tips

Mental maths is all about finding patterns, using number facts, breaking up numbers and rounding. Try different methods to find a way that works for you – everyone's strategies will be slightly different, so don't be afraid to experiment!

Get started

There are lots of different mental strategies for subtracting numbers.

- To subtract numbers ending in 9, round and adjust the answer.

  $64 - 39 \rightarrow 64 - 40 \ (+1) \rightarrow 24 + 1 \rightarrow 25$

  $742 - 199 \rightarrow 742 - 200 \ (+1) \rightarrow 543$

  $15.6 - 8.9 \rightarrow 15.6 - 9 \ (+0.1) \rightarrow 6.6 + 0.1$
  $\rightarrow 6.7$

- Use number facts to help with other subtractions.

  $15 - 8 = 7$

  $1.5 - 0.8 = 0.7$

  $1500 - 800 = 700$

- Count on from the smallest number. This number line shows how to work out $154 - 87$.

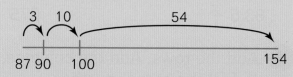

Count on from 87 to 90 and then on to 100. Hold the 3 and the 10 in your head.

100 to 154 is 54.
$54 + 10 + 3$ is 67.
So $154 - 87 = 67$

Practice

1 Try to answer each block as quickly as you can.

a $130 - 80 = $ ____

$240 - 70 = $ ____

$450 - 80 = $ ____

$370 - 90 = $ ____

$460 - 80 = $ ____

$550 - 80 = $ ____

b $94 - 49 = $ ____

$80 - 59 = $ ____

$72 - 49 = $ ____

$145 - 89 = $ ____

$108 - 69 = $ ____

$115 - 59 = $ ____

c $15.9 - 9.6 = $ ____

$18.3 - 7.4 = $ ____

$16.1 - 8.2 = $ ____

$14.8 - 6.9 = $ ____

$13.7 - 5.3 = $ ____

$25.4 - 9.6 = $ ____

d $236 - 49 = $ ____

$6.9 - 4.3 = $ ____

$4300 - 2900 = $ ____

$17.9 - 9.6 = $ ____

$256 - 69 = $ ____

$9.81 - 4.5 = $ ____

2 Write the missing numbers.

a $61 - $ _____ $= 37$

b $48 - $ _____ $= 28$

c $390 - $ _____ $= 120$

d $527 - $ _____ $= 330$

e $0.18 - $ _____ $= 0.07$

f $0.23 - $ _____ $= 0.16$

g _____ $- 47 = 39$

h _____ $- 34 = 62$

i _____ $- 260 = 380$

j _____ $- 670 = 140$

k _____ $- 0.45 = 0.18$

l _____ $- 0.36 = 0.29$

Challenge

3 Write the difference between each pair of numbers.

a
4.5	8.3	→ ___
2.9	7.4	→ ___
3.9	8.4	→ ___
6.1	9.7	→ ___
4.8	8.3	→ ___

b
27.4	29.2	→ ___
38.1	43.6	→ ___
54.8	62.5	→ ___
43.7	56.2	→ ___
76.4	88.8	→ ___

c
3100	6600	→ ___
5900	9200	→ ___
7400	2700	→ ___
5300	8900	→ ___
6200	9100	→ ___

d
1894	1902	→ ___
5189	5200	→ ___
6497	6530	→ ___
2499	2538	→ ___
7289	7304	→ ___

4 Complete each of these.

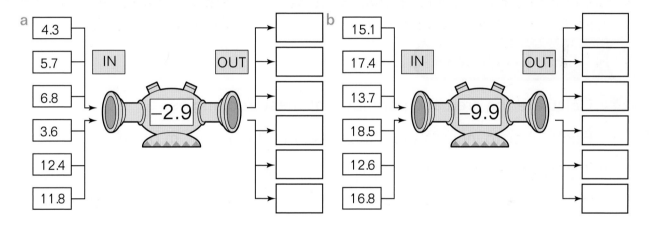

a

| 4.3 |
| 5.7 |
| 6.8 |
| 3.6 |
| 12.4 |
| 11.8 |

IN −2.9 OUT

b

| 15.1 |
| 17.4 |
| 13.7 |
| 18.5 |
| 12.6 |
| 16.8 |

IN −9.9 OUT

5 Complete each number trail from 1000 to zero.

a **1000** → − 250 → 750 → − 399 → ___ → − 240 → ___ → − 111 → **0**

b **1000** → − 698 → ___ → − 299 → ___ → − 0.98 → ___ → − 2.02 → **0**

c **1000** → − 572 → ___ → − 198 → ___ → − 187 → ___ → − 43 → **0**

d **1000** → − 867 → ___ → − 99.5 → ___ → − 19.8 → ___ → − 13.7 → **0**

Teacher's tips

Try turning subtraction problems into addition if you find addition easier. For 12 − 7 think about what you would need to add to 7 to equal 12. If you know 7 + 5 = 12, then you know 12 − 7 = 5.

Topic 4: Area and perimeter

Get started

The area of a rectangle is found by multiplying the **length** by the **width**.

14 m length

Area = 14 m × 10 m = 140 m^2

Perimeter = 2 × (14 m + 10 m) = 48 m

10 m width

The **perimeter** is the distance all the way round a shape.

To find the area and perimeter of **compound shapes**, split them into rectangles.

Practice

1 Calculate the area and perimeter of these rectangles.

Remember to include the units (mm, mm^2, cm, cm^2, m or m^2).

a 7 cm
9 cm

Area = _____

Perimeter = _____

b 3.5 cm
8 cm

Area = _____

Perimeter = _____

c 45 mm
60 mm

Area = _____

Perimeter = _____

d 18 cm
20 cm

Area = _____

Perimeter = _____

2 Calculate the area and perimeter of these shapes.

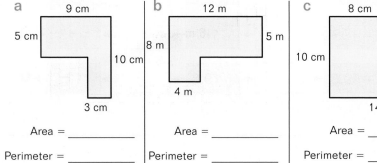

a 9 cm
5 cm
10 cm
3 cm

Area = _____

Perimeter = _____

b 12 m
8 m
5 m
4 m

Area = _____

Perimeter = _____

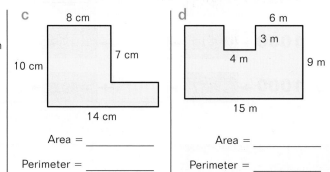

c 8 cm
10 cm
7 cm
14 cm

Area = _____

Perimeter = _____

d 6 m
3 m
4 m
9 m
15 m

Area = _____

Perimeter = _____

3 The area of the rectangle is 4 cm × 6 cm = 24 cm²
   The area of the triangle is **half** that of the rectangle. $\frac{1}{2}$ of 24 cm² is 12 cm².

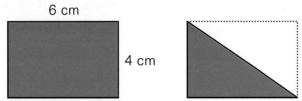

6 cm

4 cm

Work out the area of these triangles.

a
5 cm
10 cm
Area = ⬚

b
6 cm
6 cm
Area = ⬚

c
8 cm
16 cm
Area = ⬚

d
10 cm
14 cm
Area = ⬚

e
12 cm
12 cm
Area = ⬚

f
24 cm
18 cm
Area = ⬚

g
20 cm
14 cm
Area = ⬚

h
8 cm
7 cm
Area = ⬚

4 Calculate the area of each part of this garden.

Area of whole garden = _____

Area of paving = _____

Area of lawn = _____

Area of pond = _____

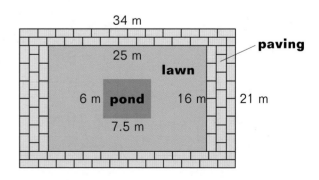

34 m
25 m
paving
lawn
6 m **pond** 16 m 21 m
7.5 m

Teacher's tips

The secret to calculating areas and perimeters is being methodical and making notes on the diagrams, especially when splitting compound shapes into several rectangles. Make lots of notes, especially of the smaller lengths and areas when you split shapes.

Topic 5: Multiplication and division facts

Get started

You should be able to work out tables quickly in your head.

- Use the tables facts to work out trickier questions.

$$6 \times 7 = 42$$
$$0.6 \times 7 = 4.2$$
$$0.6 \times 0.7 = 0.42$$

- Doubling or halving can help.

$$6 \times 8 = 48$$
$$12 \times 8 = 96$$

$152 \div 4 \rightarrow$ try halving 152, i.e.76, and halving again $\rightarrow$ 38

- Check division by multiplying.

$63 \div 9 = 7$ Check: $7 \times 9 = 63$
$56 \div 7 = 8$ Check: $8 \times 7 = 56$

- $1 \times 1 = 1$
  $2 \times 2 = 4$
  $3 \times 3 = 9$

These are the first three square numbers. They are also written as $1^2, 2^2, 3^2, \ldots$

Practice

1. Time how long it takes you to answer each block. Try to beat your best time.

a	b	c	d
$5 \times 9 = $ ___	$11 \times 6 = $ ___	$49 \div 7 = $ ___	$66 \div 6 = $ ___
$6 \times 7 = $ ___	$7 \times 7 = $ ___	$21 \div 3 = $ ___	$48 \div 8 = $ ___
$8 \times 8 = $ ___	$5 \times 12 = $ ___	$63 \div 9 = $ ___	$48 \div 4 = $ ___
$3 \times 9 = $ ___	$4 \times 8 = $ ___	$42 \div 6 = $ ___	$81 \div 9 = $ ___
$5 \times 8 = $ ___	$7 \times 11 = $ ___	$56 \div 8 = $ ___	$84 \div 7 = $ ___
$4 \times 9 = $ ___	$8 \times 7 = $ ___	$28 \div 4 = $ ___	$72 \div 6 = $ ___
$6 \times 3 = $ ___	$9 \times 8 = $ ___	$64 \div 8 = $ ___	$54 \div 9 = $ ___
$9 \times 9 = $ ___	$12 \times 6 = $ ___	$36 \div 4 = $ ___	$110 \div 10 = $ ___
$7 \times 9 = $ ___	$11 \times 10 = $ ___	$72 \div 9 = $ ___	$108 \div 9 = $ ___
$8 \times 6 = $ ___	$9 \times 12 = $ ___	$42 \div 7 = $ ___	$63 \div 7 = $ ___

2. Write the square numbers.

a $5^2 \rightarrow$ ___ b $8^2 \rightarrow$ ___ c $9^2 \rightarrow$ ___ d $6^2 \rightarrow$ ___ e $7^2 \rightarrow$ ___

f $10^2 \rightarrow$ ___ g $12^2 \rightarrow$ ___ h $20^2 \rightarrow$ ___ i $11^2 \rightarrow$ ___ j $30^2 \rightarrow$ ___

Challenge

3 Write the missing numbers.

a	____ × 0.7 = 2.1	b	____ × 0.4 = 6.4	c	____ × 0.9 = 0.81
d	____ ÷ 3 = 2.5	e	____ ÷ 5 = 0.2	f	12 × ____ = 132
g	7 × ____ = 3.5	h	0.8 × ____ = 0.16	i	110 ÷ ____ = 10
j	270 ÷ ____ = 30	k	0.4 × 0.8 = ____	l	90 × 50 = ____
m	6 × 0.7 = ____	n	172 ÷ 4 = ____	o	39 ÷ 6 = ____

4 Complete each table.

a

IN → Double → OUT

IN	47		0.16		4800		12.7	
OUT		114		680		8.5		81

b

IN → Halve → OUT

IN	0.9			570		6500		17.8	
OUT		172		0.85		109		0.07

5 Complete these grids.

a

×	7	9	6
5	35		
9			
8			

b

×	0.4	0.9	0.3
6			
7			
5			

c

×		1.4	1.9
6			
		11.2	
4	5.2		

d

×	0.5	0.7	
		0.56	
	0.2		
0.3			0.18

Teacher's tips

Learning every times table is extremely hard. Instead learn key multiplication facts (3x, 5x, 10x and its square) then calculate others from the nearest fact you know. 10 x 7 = 70, so it's easy to calculate 9 x 7 as 7 less than 70 and so on.

Topic 6: 2D shapes

Get started

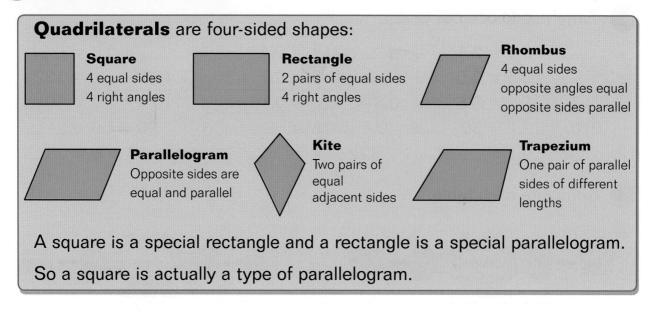

Quadrilaterals are four-sided shapes:

Square
4 equal sides
4 right angles

Rectangle
2 pairs of equal sides
4 right angles

Rhombus
4 equal sides
opposite angles equal
opposite sides parallel

Parallelogram
Opposite sides are
equal and parallel

Kite
Two pairs of
equal
adjacent sides

Trapezium
One pair of parallel
sides of different
lengths

A square is a special rectangle and a rectangle is a special parallelogram.

So a square is actually a type of parallelogram.

Practice

1 Look at the shapes and complete this chart by ticking the names.

Remember: some shapes will have more than one name.

Shape	A	B	C	D	E	F	G	H
Square								
Rhombus								
Rectangle								
Parallelogram								
Trapezium								
Kite								

A

B

C

D

E

F

G

H

Challenge

2 Tick the odd one out in each set. Name the sets.

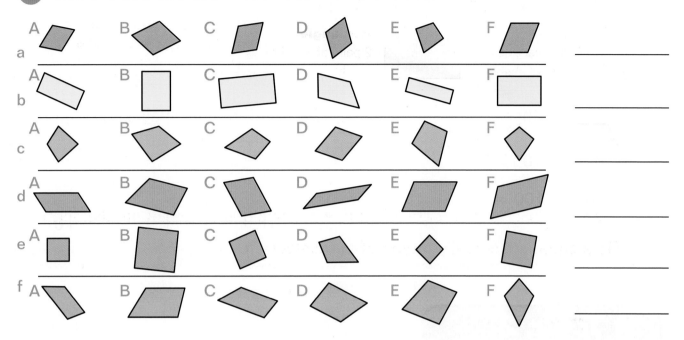

3 Write the letter for each shape in the correct place on the Venn diagram.

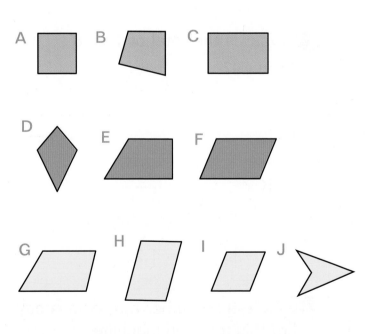

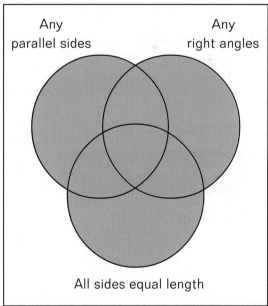

Topic 1

1 What is the value of the digit 3 in this number?

6.053 ⟶ [ ]

2 Write these as decimals.

$\frac{35}{100}$ = [ ]

$\frac{285}{1000}$ = [ ]

3 Answer these.

0.59 × 100 = [ ]

8.2 ÷ 100 = [ ]

4 Write the decimals shown on this number line.

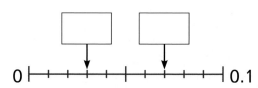

Topic 2

5 Write the total.

740 + 80 = [ ]

6 Write the missing number.

[ ] + 0.07 = 1

7 Answer this.

8.3 + 7.5 = [ ]

8 What is the total of 17, 18 and 19? [ ]

Topic 3

9 Answer this.

147 − 89 = [ ]

10 Write the missing number.

3.8 − [ ] = 1.25

11 What is the difference between 3489 and 3504?

[ ]

12 Write the number that comes out of this function machine.

Topic 4

Look at this rectangle.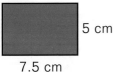

5 cm

7.5 cm

13 What is its area? _____

14 What is its perimeter? _____

Look at this shape.

2 m

5 m

3 m

6 m

15 What is its area? _____

16 What is its perimeter? _____

Topic 5

17 Answer these.

$12 \times 6 = \boxed{}$ $11 \times 12 = \boxed{}$

19 $\boxed{} \div 4 = 0.6$

18 Write the missing number.

$2.6 \times \boxed{} = 10.4$

20 What is 9^2? $\boxed{}$

Topic 6

21 What are these shapes? _____

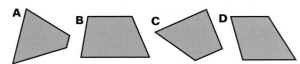

Tick the shape with a right angle.

22 Write two names for this shape.

_____

_____

23 Tick the odd one out.

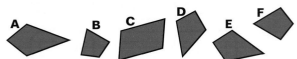

24 Draw the lines of symmetry.

Mark the test. Remember to fill in your score on page 3.

Write your score out of 24. ☐

Add a bonus point if you scored 20 or more.

TOTAL SCORE FOR TEST 1 ☐

Topic 7: Time

Get started

a.m. means ante meridiem or morning — from 12 midnight to 12 noon
p.m. means post meridiem or afternoon — from 12 noon to 12 midnight
So 7.45 a.m. is 07:45 and 7.45 p.m. is 19:45.

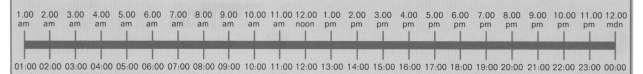

1.00 am	2.00 am	3.00 am	4.00 am	5.00 am	6.00 am	7.00 am	8.00 am	9.00 am	10.00 am	11.00 am	12.00 noon	1.00 pm	2.00 pm	3.00 pm	4.00 pm	5.00 pm	6.00 pm	7.00 pm	8.00 pm	9.00 pm	10.00 pm	11.00 pm	12.00 mdn
01:00	02:00	03:00	04:00	05:00	06:00	07:00	08:00	09:00	10:00	11:00	12:00	13:00	14:00	15:00	16:00	17:00	18:00	19:00	20:00	21:00	22:00	23:00	00:00

You always use 4 figures when you write 24-hour clock times.

Practice

1 Write these as 24-hour clock times.

a 8.25 a.m. →_____   b 4.35 p.m. →_____   c 7.55 p.m. →_____   d 10.05 a.m. →_____

e 9.53 p.m. →_____   f 2.17 a.m. →_____   g 11.28 a.m. →_____   h 10.34 p.m. →_____

i 1.23 a.m. →_____   j 8.59 p.m. →_____   k 9.14 a.m. →_____   l 11.42 p.m. →_____

2 Write these as a.m. or p.m. times.

a 06:35 →_____   b 13:45 →_____   c 19:10 →_____   d 08:05 →_____

e 12:38 →_____   f 10:41 →_____   g 15:52 →_____   h 21:13 →_____

i 01:11 →_____   j 23:46 →_____   k 11:19 →_____   l 22:53 →_____

3 Draw hands to show the times.

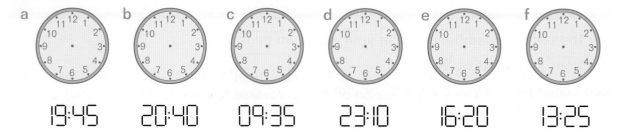

a 19:45   b 20:40   c 09:35   d 23:10   e 16:20   f 13:25

4 Write these times in order.

| 4.56 p.m. | 09:45 | 6.50 a.m. | 19:13 | 9.10 p.m. |

| 21:06 | 02:15 | 15:28 | 12.41 p.m. | 3.17 a.m. |

midnight   midnight

_____ _____ _____ _____ _____ _____ _____ _____ _____ _____

5 A bus takes 18 minutes between each stop. Complete the timetable.

Moss Lane	08:45	11:22		
Brook Street	09:03		16:40	
Church Road		11:58		
Beck Avenue				22:05

6 These clocks are all running fast. If the real time is 1.45 p.m., how many minutes fast is each clock?

a

☐ minutes fast

b

☐ minutes fast

c

☐ minutes fast

d

☐ minutes fast

e

☐ minutes fast

f

☐ minutes fast

Teacher's tips

A quick way to change 12-hour time into 24-hour is to add 12 to the hours if it's 'p.m.', and nothing if it's 'a.m.'. You can also do this in reverse to change 24-hour times into 12-hour times.

Topic 8: Fractions

Get started

A fraction has two parts.

$\frac{2}{5}$ ← **numerator**
← **denominator**

Here are 3 types of fraction:

- A **proper fraction**, such as $\frac{3}{5}$, which is less than 1
- An **improper fraction**, such as $\frac{7}{3}$, which is greater than 1
- A **mixed number**, such as $4\frac{3}{8}$, which has whole numbers and fractions.

Fractions that have the same value are called **equivalent fractions**.
$\frac{2}{3}$ is the same as $\frac{6}{9}$

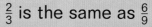

A fraction can be changed into its equivalent by either multiplying or dividing the numerator and denominator by the same number.

$\frac{2 \times 3}{3 \times 3} = \frac{6}{9}$ $\frac{18 \div 3}{21 \div 3} = \frac{6}{7}$

Practice

1 Change these to improper fractions.

a $2\frac{1}{5} = \boxed{}$ b $4\frac{3}{4} = \boxed{}$ c $1\frac{7}{10} = \boxed{}$ d $6\frac{1}{3} = \boxed{}$ e $2\frac{3}{8} = \boxed{}$ f $3\frac{4}{5} = \boxed{}$

g $1\frac{3}{7} = \boxed{}$ h $6\frac{1}{10} = \boxed{}$ i $4\frac{7}{12} = \boxed{}$ j $2\frac{5}{6} = \boxed{}$ k $9\frac{2}{3} = \boxed{}$ l $4\frac{5}{8} = \boxed{}$

2 Change these to mixed numbers.

a $\frac{19}{4} = \boxed{}$ b $\frac{22}{3} = \boxed{}$ c $\frac{6}{5} = \boxed{}$ d $\frac{7}{4} = \boxed{}$ e $\frac{19}{5} = \boxed{}$ f $\frac{23}{8} = \boxed{}$

g $\frac{11}{7} = \boxed{}$ h $\frac{28}{5} = \boxed{}$ i $\frac{35}{6} = \boxed{}$ j $\frac{53}{7} = \boxed{}$ k $\frac{87}{10} = \boxed{}$ l $\frac{41}{8} = \boxed{}$

3 Cancel each fraction down to make it as simple as possible.

a $\frac{24}{40} \rightarrow \boxed{}$ b $\frac{45}{90} \rightarrow \boxed{}$ c $\frac{33}{99} \rightarrow \boxed{}$ d $\frac{64}{100} \rightarrow \boxed{}$ e $\frac{24}{64} \rightarrow \boxed{}$

f $\frac{12}{16} \rightarrow \boxed{}$ g $\frac{28}{52} \rightarrow \boxed{}$ h $\frac{36}{40} \rightarrow \boxed{}$ i $\frac{15}{95} \rightarrow \boxed{}$ j $\frac{16}{80} \rightarrow \boxed{}$

4 Write the missing digits for these equivalent fractions.

a $\dfrac{3}{5} = \dfrac{\boxed{}}{10} = \dfrac{15}{\boxed{}}$

b $\dfrac{2}{3} = \dfrac{\boxed{}}{9} = \dfrac{12}{\boxed{}}$

c $\dfrac{3}{4} = \dfrac{\boxed{}}{8} = \dfrac{15}{\boxed{}}$

d $\dfrac{5}{8} = \dfrac{\boxed{}}{24} = \dfrac{25}{\boxed{}}$

e $\dfrac{3}{10} = \dfrac{\boxed{}}{30} = \dfrac{30}{\boxed{}}$

f $\dfrac{7}{8} = \dfrac{\boxed{}}{16} = \dfrac{21}{\boxed{}}$

g $\dfrac{1}{4} = \dfrac{\boxed{}}{40} = \dfrac{50}{\boxed{}}$

h $\dfrac{5}{6} = \dfrac{\boxed{}}{18} = \dfrac{40}{\boxed{}}$

i $\dfrac{3}{7} = \dfrac{\boxed{}}{21} = \dfrac{30}{\boxed{}}$

j $\dfrac{2}{5} = \dfrac{\boxed{}}{25} = \dfrac{20}{\boxed{}}$

k $\dfrac{3}{8} = \dfrac{\boxed{}}{40} = \dfrac{21}{\boxed{}}$

l $\dfrac{7}{12} = \dfrac{\boxed{}}{36} = \dfrac{35}{\boxed{}}$

5 Put each group of fractions in order, starting with the smallest.

a $\dfrac{3}{8}$ $\dfrac{7}{12}$ $\dfrac{1}{4}$

b $\dfrac{2}{3}$ $\dfrac{1}{2}$ $\dfrac{3}{5}$

c $\dfrac{5}{6}$ $\dfrac{1}{3}$ $\dfrac{1}{12}$

6 Join each of these fractions to its correct place on this number line.

$\dfrac{1}{3}$ $\dfrac{1}{2}$ $\dfrac{7}{10}$ $\dfrac{1}{5}$

$\dfrac{2}{5}$ $\dfrac{5}{6}$ $\dfrac{3}{10}$ $\dfrac{9}{10}$ $\dfrac{2}{3}$ $\dfrac{3}{5}$

0 ———————————————— 1

Teacher's tips

An 'equivalent fraction' doesn't change the actual value of a number, just how it's expressed. Whatever you do to the denominator you must also do to the numerator (or you will be changing the value of the fraction).

Topic 9: Written addition

Get started

If an addition is too difficult to add in your head, use a written method. For example, to add 46,328 and 8749:

1. Write the numbers, lining up each column.

```
  46328
+  8749
```

2. Start adding the units column. For any total over 9, put the tens digit under the next column.

```
  46328
+  8749
      7
     1
```

3. Now add the tens column. Keep going left until all the columns have been added.

```
  46328
+  8749
  55077
  1 1  1
```

Numbers that have a decimal point can be added in the same way.

Practice

1 Answer these.

a
```
  3945
+ 5680
```

b
```
  6035
+ 8985
```

c
```
  4870
+ 4693
```

d
```
  6728
+ 8740
```

e
```
  9128
+ 4675
```

f
```
45929
+ 3874
```

g
```
87263
+ 6815
```

h
```
45923
+ 3946
```

i
```
57667
+ 3843
```

j
```
  27561
+  2918
```

2 Total these amounts. Use a written method.

a £73.85   b £482.93   c £6952   d £8559.45   e £8081   f £9522.50

a   a + d →
b   b + c →
c   c + d →
d   b + a →
e   a + f →
f   e + c →
g   f + d →
h   f + c →
i   f + e →

Challenge

3 Look at the numbers and answer these.

46 385 **48 352** **46 854** **23 647** **29 967**

a What is the total of all the even numbers in this set? _____

b What is the total of all the odd numbers in this set? _____

c What is the largest total that can be made by totalling two of these numbers? _____

4 Write the missing digits in these sums.

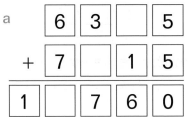

a
```
  6 3 □ 5
+ 7 □ 1 5
1 □ 7 6 0
```

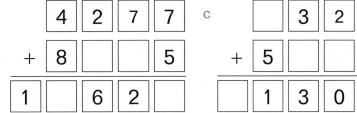

b
```
  4 2 7 7
+ 8 □ □ 5
1 □ 6 2 □
```

c
```
  □ 3 2 □
+ 5 □ □ 4
□ 1 3 0 2
```

d
```
  3 8 4 □
+ □ 6 □ 3
1 1 □ 0 0
```

e
```
  1 3 9 2 □
+ 4 □ 6 □ 3
□ 8 □ 8 2
```

5 Answer these number problems.

a The total of two numbers is 1260. One number is twice as big as the other.
What are the two numbers? _____ and _____

b The sum of three consecutive numbers is 33 333.
What are the three numbers? _____ and _____ and

_____

c The sum of two numbers is 160. The difference between them is 10.
What are the two numbers? _____ and _____

d The total of two numbers is 90 and their product is 1400.
What are the two numbers? _____ and _____

Teacher's tips

People often describe 'carrying over' numbers in long addition methods, when what they mean is that the sum of the units becomes more than 9, and therefore the 'tens' need to be added to the other tens in the appropriate column.

Get started

If a subtraction is too difficult to do in your head, use a written method. For example, to answer 6458 − 2975:

1. Write the numbers, lining up each column

```
  6 4 5 8
− 2 9 7 5
_____
```

2. Start from the right-hand column, taking away the bottom digit from the top digit.

```
  6 4 5 8
− 2 9 7 5
_____
        3
```

3. If the top digit is smaller than the bottom digit, exchange a 10 from the next column.

```
   5 13 1
  6 4̷ 5 8
− 2 9 7 5
_____
  3 4 8 3
```

Numbers that have a decimal point can be subtracted in the same way.

Practice

1 Answer these.

a 7 9 4 3
 − 5 6 8 0
_____

b 6 0 5 5
 − 2 9 4 3
_____

c 8 3 7 0
 − 5 6 9 5
_____

d 9 7 2 8
 − 4 7 8 0
_____

e 9 1 2 4
 − 8 6 7 5
_____

f 4 3 9 2 9
 −   7 8 7 9
_____

g 1 7 2 6 5
 −   6 0 1 5
_____

h 4 3 9 2 5
 −   5 9 8 6
_____

i 2 7 6 6 7
 −   5 8 0 3
_____

j 2 7 5 6 1
 −   9 9 1 8
_____

2 Work out the differences. Use pencil and paper for the subtractions.

a 184.85 kg b 382.93 kg c 1345.5 kg d 652 kg e 67.345 kg f 82.875 kg

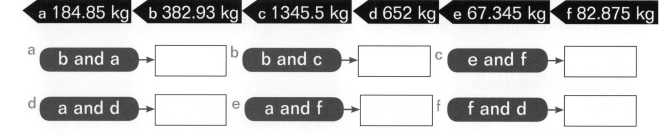

a b and a →
b b and c →
c e and f →
d a and d →
e a and f →
f f and d →

Challenge

3 Look at the numbers and answer these.

| 38 945 | 81 453 | 37 294 | 48 120 | 48 756 |

a What is the difference between the two odd numbers in this set? _____

b What is the difference between the two largest even numbers in this set? _____

c What is the difference between the two smallest numbers in this set?
_____

d Which two of these numbers have a difference of 33 333? _____

4 Write the missing digits in these subtractions.

a
```
    □ 1 7 5
  – 3 0 6 □
    5 □ 0 6
```

b
```
  1 0 □ 7 □
  – □ 5 □ 5
    □ 1 9 0 7
```

c
```
  □ 4 3 6 □
  – 7 □ □ 8
  1 6 6 8 4
```

d
```
  3 5 □ □ 4
  – 1 4 6 8 5
    2 □ 3 1 □
```

e
```
  □ □ 1 2 5
  – 1 8 6 □ □
    2 3 4 2 9
```

5 Answer these number problems.

a The difference between two numbers is 180. Their total is 400.
What are the two numbers? _____ and _____

b The difference between two numbers is 15. Their product is 700.
What are the two numbers? _____ and _____

c The difference between two numbers is 260. Their total is 960.
What are the two numbers? _____ and _____

d The difference between two numbers is 30. Their product is 5400.
What are the two numbers? _____ and _____

Teacher's tips

To find the difference between two numbers quickly subtract the smaller number from the larger number.

Get started

A number **sequence** is a list of numbers in a pattern.

To find the rule or pattern, look at the differences between the numbers.

7 $\xrightarrow{+9}$ 16 $\xrightarrow{+9}$ 25 $\xrightarrow{+9}$ 34   The rule or pattern is +9

14 $\xrightarrow{-6}$ 8 $\xrightarrow{-6}$ 2 $\xrightarrow{-6}$ -4   The rule or pattern is -6

Square numbers and **triangular numbers** make interesting patterns. Square numbers are made from growing squares.

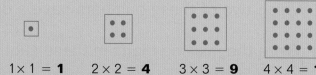

$1 \times 1 = \mathbf{1}$ $2 \times 2 = \mathbf{4}$ $3 \times 3 = \mathbf{9}$ $4 \times 4 = \mathbf{16}$

Triangular numbers are made from growing triangles.

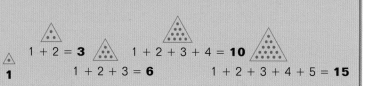

1 $1 + 2 = \mathbf{3}$ $1 + 2 + 3 = \mathbf{6}$ $1 + 2 + 3 + 4 = \mathbf{10}$ $1 + 2 + 3 + 4 + 5 = \mathbf{15}$

Practice

1 Write the next three numbers in each sequence.

a 4, 19, 34, _____, _____, _____   b 89, 78, 67, _____, _____, _____

c 19, 38, 57, _____, _____, _____   d 42, 34, 26, _____, _____, _____

e 125, 100, 75, _____, _____, _____   f 100, 93, 86, _____, _____, _____

g 39, 33, 27, _____, _____, _____   h 21, 42, 63, _____, _____, _____

i 95, 80, 65, _____, _____, _____   j 900, 875, 850, _____, _____, _____

2 Write the missing numbers in each sequence.

a −16, −4, _____, 20, _____, _____   b _____, −13, −7, −1, _____, _____

c _____, _____, 0, _____, 30, 45   d −12, −1, _____, _____, 32, _____

e _____, _____, _____, −1, 8, 17   f _____, −30, −15, _____, _____, 30

g _____, −55, −49, _____, −37, _____   h −24, _____, _____, 12, 24, _____

i _____, _____, −61, −42, −23, _____   j −70, −55, _____, _____, _____, 5

Challenge

3 Draw the next set of dot patterns and write the numbers for each.

a   [ ] ____ ____ ____ ____

b   [ ] ____ ____ ____ ____

c   [ ] ____ ____ ____ ____

4 Continue these sequences.

a 1, 4, 9, 16, _____, _____, _____   b 1, 3, 6, 10, _____, _____, _____

c 1, 1, 2, 3, 5, _____, _____, _____

Write the 10th number in each sequence.

a _____   b _____   c _____

5 These are the digital roots for the 2x table. The digits are added together: e.g. the digital root of 12 = 1 + 2 = 3.

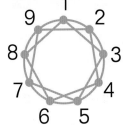

× 2	2	4	6	8	10	12	14	16	18	20
digital roots	2	4	6	8	1	3	5	7	9	2

The digital roots for the 2x table are joined in order on this circle.

Now try the same thing for the digital roots of the 3x, 4x and 5x tables.

Look for patterns in your results.

a **3x** 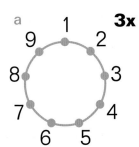   b **4x** 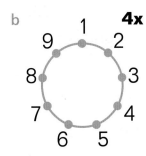   c **5x**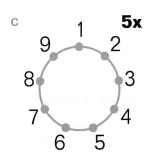

Topic 12: Comparing and ordering numbers

Get started

When you need to put decimals in order, it is helpful to write them under each other, lining up the decimal points.

For example

6.57 6.658 16.07 16.7 ⟶ **6.57**

6.658

16.07

16.7

< means **is less than**

For example 3.85 < 3.9

3.85 is less than 3.9

> means **is greater than**

For example 8.24 > 8.19

8.24 is greater than 8.19

Practice

1 Write these numbers in order, starting with the smallest.

a 3.64, 3.86, 3.48, 4.06

———, ———, ———, ———

b 4.87, 4.78, 4.46, 5.49

———, ———, ———, ———

c 6.49, 6.79, 9.05, 6.98

———, ———, ———, ———

d 2.17, 7.12, 7.22, 2.87

———, ———, ———, ———

e 31.27, 37.8, 27.09, 31.72

———, ———, ———, ———

f 17.86, 16.78, 75.11, 75.89

———, ———, ———, ———

g 0.454, 0.467, 0.458, 0.457

———, ———, ———, ———

h 3.243, 2.445, 3.036, 3.321,

———, ———, ———, ———

2 Write the sign < or > for each pair of numbers.

a 3.45 __ 4.26

b 8.14 __ 8.41

c 5.36 __ 5.35

d 8.17 __ 8.3

e 0.93 __ 0.9

f 24.53 __ 25.43

g 1.633 __ 1.64

h 4.978 __ 4.987

i 7.038 __ 7.86

Challenge

3 Write the halfway number on each of these number lines.

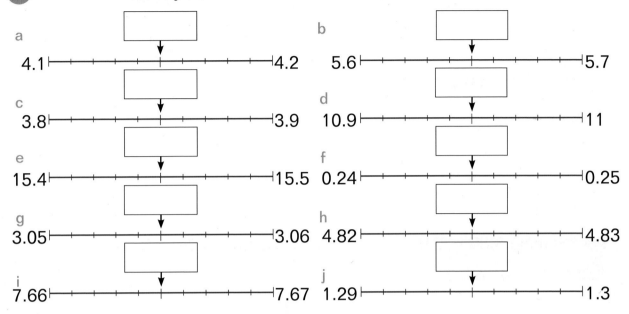

a
4.1 ⊢——————————⊣ 4.2

b
5.6 ⊢——————————⊣ 5.7

c
3.8 ⊢——————————⊣ 3.9

d
10.9 ⊢——————————⊣ 11

e
15.4 ⊢——————————⊣ 15.5

f
0.24 ⊢——————————⊣ 0.25

g
3.05 ⊢——————————⊣ 3.06

h
4.82 ⊢——————————⊣ 4.83

i
7.66 ⊢——————————⊣ 7.67

j
1.29 ⊢——————————⊣ 1.3

4 Write the signs < or > for these.

a 6.02 __ 6.68 __ 7.58   b 7.99 __ 7.09 __ 7.94 c 8.4 __ 8.06 __ 8.61

d 7.664 __ 7.846 __ 7.688 e 2.795 __ 2.8 __ 2.75 f 6.957 __ 6.095 __ 6.288

5 These are the times of the runners in the London 2012 Olympic 100m final. Write them in order, starting with the fastest.

Athlete	Time (seconds)	Athlete	Time (seconds)
BAILEY Ryan	9.88		
BLAKE Yohan	9.75		
BOLT Usain	9.63		
GATLIN Justin	9.79		
GAY Tyson	9.80		
MARTINA Churandy	9.94		
THOMPSON Richard	9.98		

Teacher's tips

What would the answer be if there wasn't a decimal point? Check that your answer looks right. Remember the importance of place value, and that if you need to, you can write the answer to more digital places than the question.

Test 2 (Score 1 mark for every correct answer)

Topic 7

1 Write as 24-hour clock times.

10.28 p.m. →

9.52 a.m. →

2 Write these times as a.m. or p.m.

10:41 →

20:07 →

3 Draw hands to show this time.

4 A clock is 12 minutes slow. If it shows 14:56, what is the real time? _____

Topic 8

5 Change this to an improper fraction.

$7\frac{4}{5} =$

6 Change this to a mixed number.

$\frac{47}{6} =$

7 Write the equivalent fractions.

$\frac{3}{8} = \frac{\square}{40} = \frac{12}{\square}$

8 Cancel this fraction to make it simple as as possible.

$\frac{20}{85} =$

Topic 9

9 Answer this.

```
  5 9 8 6 5
+ 8 6 9 3 7
```

10 Answer this.

```
  6 0 8 . 4 5
+ 7 2 8 . 5 9
```

11 What is the total of these two numbers?

3985 + 9250 = _____

12 What is the sum of these three amounts?

£46.98 + £345.09 + £578.65 = _____

Topic 10

13 Answer this.

```
  3 5 2 0 5
-     8 6 9 7
_____
```

14 What is the difference between

13 403 and 7815? _____

15 Answer this.

```
  4 6 1 . 2 5
- 2 9 3 . 4 6
_____
```

16 Write the missing digits.

6		1		4
	6		2	9

| 1 | 3 | 3 | 0 | |

Topic 11

17 Write the next three numbers in this sequence.

17, 28, 39, 50, ___, ___, ___

18 Write the missing numbers in this sequence.

−25, −16, ___, 2, ___, ___

19 Write the four missing numbers.

___, ___, 36, 49, 64 ___, ___

Name this sequence: _____

20 Write the four missing numbers.

___, ___, 21, 28, 36, 45, ___, ___

Name this sequence: _____

Topic 12

21 Write the signs < or >
71.04 ___ 72.59 ___ 72.6

22 Write the signs < or >
31.05 ___ 31.5   0.345 ___ 0.335

23 Write the halfway number.

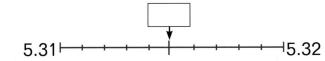

5.31 ├─┼─┼─┼─┼─┼─┼─┼─┤ 5.32

24 Write these numbers in order, starting with the smallest.
58.69, 5.899, 56.89, 8.659, 5.868

_____, _____, _____, _____, _____

Mark the test. Remember to fill in your score on page 3.

Write your score out of 24.

Add a bonus point if you scored 20 or more.

TOTAL SCORE FOR TEST 2

Topic 13: Rounding numbers

Get started

Rounding decimals makes them easier to work with.

You can round them to the nearest whole number or the nearest tenth.

Rounding is useful for estimating approximate answers.

Rounding to the nearest whole number

- Look at the **tenths** digit
- If it is 5 or more, round up to the next whole number
- If it is less than 5, the units digit stays the same

   7.5 rounds up to 8

   6.47 rounds down to 6

Rounding to the nearest tenth

- Look at the **hundredths** digit
- If it is 5 or more, round up to the next tenth
- If it is less than 5, the tenths digit stays the same

   3.86 rounds up to 3.9

   5.437 rounds down to 5.4

Practice

1 Round these to the nearest whole number.

a 45.6 → _____   b 28.3 → _____   c 14.9 → _____

d 30.5 → _____   e 64.4 → _____   f 83.8 → _____

g 14.84 → _____   h 92.61 → _____   i 79.55 → _____

j 3.046 → _____   k 8.454 → _____   l 9.518 → _____

2 Round these to the nearest tenth.

a 7.53 → _____   b 4.55 → _____   c 1.45 → _____

d 5.76 → _____   e 8.17 → _____   f 9.36 → _____

g 6.914 → _____   h 5.845 → _____   i 0.783 → _____

j 4.138 → _____   k 3.865 → _____   l 2.757 → _____

Challenge

3 Estimate which decimal number each arrow points to.

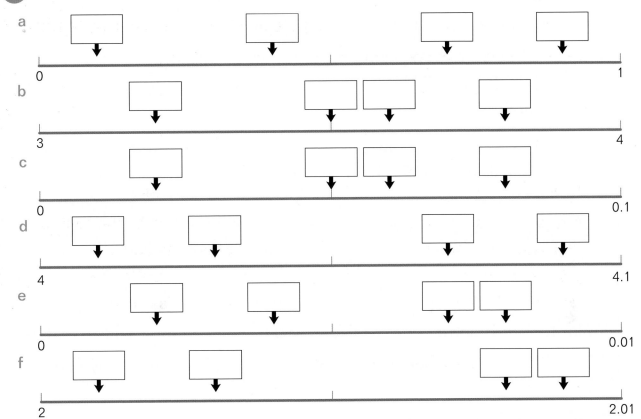

4 Estimate approximate answers to these.

a   Round these to the nearest whole number.

16.9 + 4.34 → _____

32.08 + 63.6 → _____

83.3 − 59.8 → _____

76.6 − 33.4 → _____

3.3 × 4.9 → _____

6.7 × 8.4 → _____

b   Round these to the nearest tenth.

6.738 + 14.49 → _____

61.53 + 36.34 → _____

58.69 − 43.65 → _____

73.51 − 61.38 → _____

0.45 × 0.81 → _____

5.14 × 3.06 → _____

Teacher's tips

5 and above rounds up (even 5.001); *anything* less than 5 (even 4.999) rounds down.
Think of it as adding or subtracting to get to the closest factor of 10 (or 100, 1000).

Topic 14: Measures

Get started

Don't forget these metric measures.

1000 metres = 1 kilometre

1000 millimetres = 1 metre

100 centimetres = 1 metre

10 decimetres = 1 metre

1000 grams = 1 kilogram

1000 kg = 1 tonne

1000 millilitres = 1 litre

100 centilitres = 1 litre

10 decilitres = 1 litre

We used **imperial measures** in the past. We still sometimes use pints, gallons, pounds, inches and feet, so it is useful to know their values.

Length	Weight	Capacity
12 inches = 1 foot	16 ounces = 1 pound (lb)	8 pints = 1 gallon
2.5 cm ≈ 1 inch	30 g ≈ 1 ounce	1.75 pints ≈ 1 litre
30 cm ≈ 1 foot	2.25 lb ≈ 1 kg	4.5 litres ≈ 1 gallon
3.25 feet ≈ 1 metre	1 lb ≈ 450 g	1 pint ≈ 600 ml

1.6 km ≈ 1 mile   Remember that ≈ means "is approximately equal to".

Practice

1 Convert these metric measures.

a _____ cm = 4.2 metres

b _____ mm = 5 centimetres

c _____ m = 12 kilometres

d _____ dm = 8.5 metres

e _____ g = 40 kilograms

f _____ kg = 4.5 tonnes

g _____ ml = 18 litres

h _____ cl = 3.9 litres

i _____ dl = 5.2 litres

j _____ mm = 3.8 metres

k _____ ml = 7 decilitres

l _____ cl = 4 decilitres

2 Write these as approximate measures.

a 10 cm ≈ _____ inches

b _____ g ≈ 4 ounces

c 18 litres ≈ _____ gallons

d 17.5 pints ≈ _____ litres

e 18 lb ≈ _____ kg

f 8 km ≈ _____ miles

Challenge

3 Change these to approximate metric units.

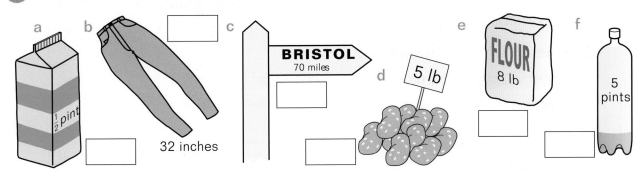

4 Tick ☑ the longer length for each of these.

a 80 cm ☐ or 3 feet ☐   b 10 inches ☐ or 2000 mm ☐

c 25 km ☐ or 20 miles ☐   d 2 feet ☐ or 500 mm ☐

e 15 m ☐ or 40 feet ☐   f 8 feet ☐ or 100 inches ☐

5

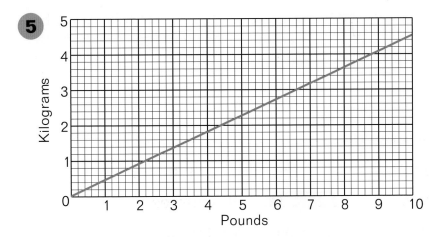

Look at this approximate conversion graph for pounds to kilograms.
1 pound ≈ 0.45 kg

Use the graph to complete this table. These conversions are approximate.

Pounds	1	2		0.5		10		8
Kilograms	0.45		2.25		3.4		4	

Teacher's tips

Most rulers and tape measures show metric and imperial measurements. Start to look at both when measuring so you begin to know the approximate values of each (for instance, a standard 30cm ruler is approximately 12 inches, or 1 foot).

Topic 15: 3D shapes

Get started

Polyhedra are 3D shapes made from lots of polygons.
Each polyhedron has

- **faces** which are flat and are polygons
- **edges** which are straight lines where two faces meet
- **vertices** which are the points where three or more edges meet.

The **net** of a shape is what it looks like when it is opened out flat.

This is a net of a cube.

Practice

1 Name each of these shapes.

a   b   c   d   e   f

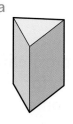 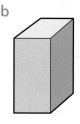   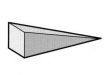 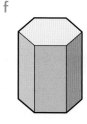

_____   _____   _____   _____   _____   _____

_____   _____   _____   _____   _____   _____

2 Join these descriptions to the correct names.

12 pentagonal faces

4 triangular faces

1 square face and 4 triangular faces

4 rectangular faces and 2 square faces

Cuboid

Cube

Tetrahedron

Triangular prism

Square-based pyramid

Octahedron

Pentagonal prism

Dodecahedron

8 triangular faces

2 triangular faces and 3 rectangular faces

6 square faces

2 pentagonal faces and 5 rectangular faces

Challenge

3 Write the name of each of these shapes from its net.

a

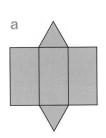

_____

b

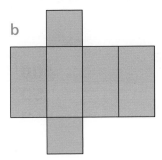

_____

c

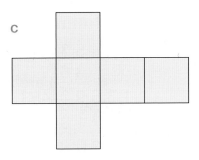

_____

d

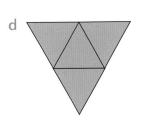

_____

e

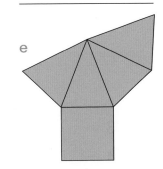

_____

f

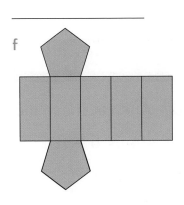

_____

4 Each polyhedron has a number of faces, edges and vertices. Complete this chart for each shape and see if you can spot a rule or pattern between the numbers.

Name of shape	Number of faces	Number of edges	Number of vertices
Cuboid	6	12	8
Tetrahedron			
Square-based pyramid			
Pentagonal prism			
Triangular prism			
Dodecahedron			
Octahedron			

Rule: _____

Teacher's tips

Practise working out 3D shapes from their nets by cutting them out of squared paper and building them. Start from the outside and fold up along each line. This will help you to visualise other shapes from their net diagrams.

Get started

Here are two ways to work out **453 × 36**.

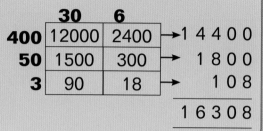

Column method		Grid method
4 5 3		
× 3 6		
1 3 5 9 0 453 × 30		
2 7 1 8 453 × 6		
1 6 3 0 8		

	30	**6**	
400	12000	2400	→1 4 4 0 0
50	1500	300	→ 1 8 0 0
3	90	18	→ 1 0 8
			1 6 3 0 8

Practice

1 Answer these mentally.

a 400 × 5 = _____   b 600 × 8 = _____   c 700 × 5 = _____

d 700 × 2 = _____   e 900 × 4 = _____   f 600 × 5 = _____

g 900 × 6 = _____   h 800 × 9 = _____   i 800 × 7 = _____

j 700 × 3 = _____   k 200 × 80 = _____   l 400 × 70 = _____

2 Use the grid method to answer these.

a 48 × 63

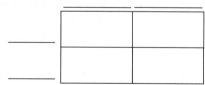

The total is _____

b 184 × 52

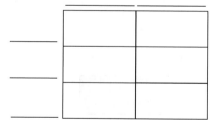

The total is _____

3 Use the column method to answer these.

a
```
        56
×       48
_____

_____
```

b
```
       3 1 4
×        5 7
_____

_____
```

c
```
       5 3 9
×        8 4
_____

_____
```

Challenge

4 Choose a written method to answer these.

a 79 × 45 b 68 × 83 c 537 × 9 d 244 × 6 e 609 × 58 f 476 × 74

_____ _____ _____ _____ _____ _____

5 Answer these problems.

a Mr Owen pays £85 a month into a savings account.
How much does he save in a year? _____

b There are 96 pages in a maths book with 36 sums on each page.
How many sums are there in the book? _____

c There are 47 coaches, each seating 52 passengers. If all the coaches are
full, how many passengers are there altogether? _____

d One chocolate bar weighs 186 g.
How much would a box of 9 chocolate bars weigh? _____

e A plane ticket costs £278.
What would be the total cost for four tickets? _____

6 Calculate the area of each rectangle. Write an estimate first.

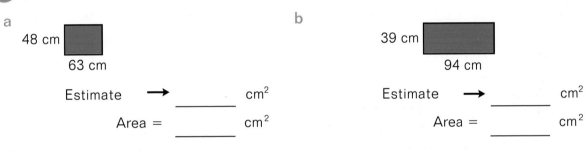

a
48 cm
63 cm

Estimate ⟶ _____ cm²

Area = _____ cm²

b
39 cm
94 cm

Estimate ⟶ _____ cm²

Area = _____ cm²

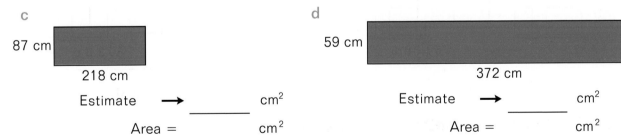

c
87 cm
218 cm

Estimate ⟶ _____ cm²

Area = _____ cm²

d
59 cm
372 cm

Estimate ⟶ _____ cm²

Area = _____ cm²

Teacher's tips

Choose a method that makes sense to you and practise it as much as you can,
making notes so you can check it easily. Get into the habit of estimating answers first
by rounding numbers to the nearest 10.

Get started

There are several ways of writing a division **384 ÷ 6**.

```
  6) 3 8 4
   - 3 0 0    6 × 50
       8 4
     - 6 0    6 × 10
       2 4
     - 2 4    6 ×  4
       = 64
```

```
       6 4
  6) 3 8 ²4
```

Sometimes divisions aren't exact and leave **remainders**.

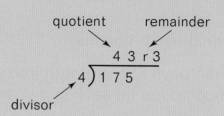

```
quotient        remainder

        4 3 r 3
  4) 1 7 5

divisor
```

Practice

1 Answer these mentally.

a 280 ÷ 4 = _____　　b 190 ÷ 2 = _____　　c 310 ÷ 5 = _____

d 700 ÷ 4 = _____　　e 270 ÷ 3 = _____　　f 600 ÷ 5 = _____

g 540 ÷ 6 = _____　　h 450 ÷ 9 = _____　　i 940 ÷ 5 = _____

j 640 ÷ 4 = _____　　k 720 ÷ 3 = _____　　l 210 ÷ 7 = _____

m 560 ÷ 8 = _____　　n 280 ÷ 4 = _____　　o 970 ÷ 5 = _____

2 Answer these. Remember to include the remainder.

a ☐☐ r☐
4) 2 8 7

b ☐☐ r☐
6) 1 6 5

c ☐☐ r☐
5) 7 4 3

d ☐☐ r☐
8) 3 8 6

e ☐☐ r☐
3) 4 9 6

f ☐☐ r☐
5) 3 2 7

g ☐☐ r☐
6) 2 9 8

h ☐☐ r☐
9) 6 4 5

i ☐☐ r☐
3) 7 9 0

j ☐☐ r☐
7) 8 4 5

Challenge

3 Answer these problems.

a There are 366 days in a leap year. How many full weeks are there in a leap year and how many days are left over? _____ weeks and _____ days

b What number is one-quarter of 748? _____

c There are 257 children in a school. They are divided into four groups – three equal groups and one with an extra child.
How many children are in the group with one extra child? _____

d What is the quotient of 9 and 378? _____

e I have 238 sweets. Each box holds 8 sweets.
How many boxes will I need? _____

f A gym costs £9 each week. Sam has paid £750.
How many weeks does this pay for? _____

4 Match each division to a remainder.
Write a division for the spare remainder in the empty box.

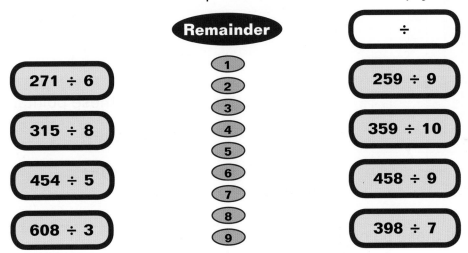

Remainder

271 ÷ 6		259 ÷ 9
315 ÷ 8		359 ÷ 10
454 ÷ 5		458 ÷ 9
608 ÷ 3		398 ÷ 7

1 2 3 4 5 6 7 8 9

÷

5 Write the missing digits 1 to 6 to complete these divisions.

1 **2** **3** **4** **5** **6**

a 59◯ ÷ 4 = ◯48

b 47◯ ÷ 3 = 1◯8 r 2

c ◯89 ÷ 5 = 77 r◯

Teacher's tips

A lot of division problems require you to use your common sense as well as your mathematical abilities – remember to think about whether the answer makes sense in the real world. For instance, can you have $\frac{1}{2}$ a person?

Topic 18: Coordinates

Get started

Coordinates show the exact position of a point on a grid.

Negative numbers can be used to show positions.

The coordinates of A are $(-3, -2)$
The coordinates of B are $(2, -3)$
The coordinates of C are $(-4, -1)$

Read the **horizontal** coordinate first and then the **vertical** coordinate.

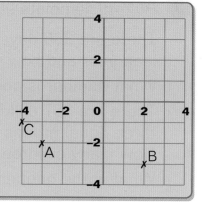

Practice

1 Look at these points and answer the questions.

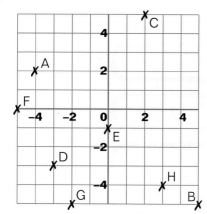

Write the coordinates of these points.

A → (___,___)   C → (___,___)

E → (___,___)   G → (___,___)

Write the letter for each of these points.

$(5, -5)$ → _____ $(-5, 0)$ → _____

$(-3, -3)$ → _____ $(3, -4)$ → _____

2 Plot and label these points on the grid.

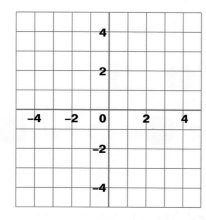

A = $(-4, 2)$ B = $(3, 5)$

C = $(0, -1)$ D = $(-2, -2)$

E = $(3, -5)$ F = $(5, 0)$

G = $(-3, -4)$ H = $(-2, 5)$

Challenge

3 Plot these points and join them in order.

Name the two types of triangle.

Triangle 1 (−5, 2) (0, 4) (5, 2): _____

Triangle 2 (−3, −1) (−3, −5) (5, −5):

_____

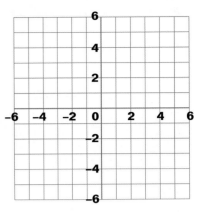

4 Here are three corners of a rectangle.

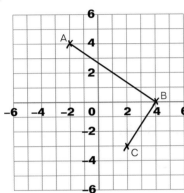

What are the coordinates of the three corners?

A →(___,___) B →(___,___) C →(___,___)

What are the coordinates of the fourth corner, D?

(___,___)

Plot the point and complete the rectangle.

5 These are two corners of a quadrilateral.

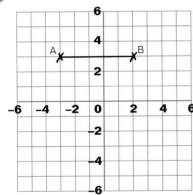

What are the coordinates of

Point A →(___,___)

Point B →(___,___)

The coordinates of the other two corners are

Point C →(4, −4)

Point D →(−3, −2)

Plot points C and D and draw the shape.

Name the shape: _____

Topic 13

1 Round these to the nearest whole number. 16.47 → _____

83.62 → _____

2 Round these to the nearest tenth. 1.754 → _____

4.082 → _____

3 Estimate which number each arrow points to.

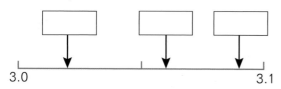

3.0   3.1

4 Estimate these to the nearest whole number.

45.48 + 37.6 → _____

94.09 − 61.83 → _____

Topic 14

5 Write the equivalent length.

255 cm = _____ metres

6 Write this as kilograms.

4320 g = _____ kg

7 Convert this amount.

_____ litres ≈ 10 gallons

8 Tick the longer length.

35 km ☐ or 60 miles ☐

Topic 15

9 Name this shape.

_____

10 Which shape has 2 triangular faces and 3 rectangular faces?

_____

11 Which shape is made by this net?

_____

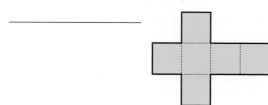

12 Complete this:

A square-based pyramid has __ faces, __ edges and __ vertices.

Topic 16

13 Answer this using the column method.

$$
\begin{array}{r}
4\,6\,9 \\
\times\ \ \ 5\,3 \\
\hline
\\
\hline
\end{array}
$$

14 Answer this using the grid method.

785 × 36

_____

_____

the total is ___

15 Write the answer.

700 × 30 = _____

16 A packet of biscuits weighs 274 g. They are packed in boxes of 64. What is the total weight of a box? _____

Topic 17

17 Write the answer.

480 ÷ 4 = _____

18 Answer this. $6\overline{)378}$

19 Answer this. $9\overline{)742}$

20 £3.50 ÷ 6 objects = ⬚ and 2p change

Topic 18

Look at these points and answer the questions.

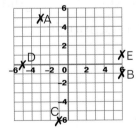

21 Write the coordinates of A → (___,___)

22 What letter is at (6, −1) → _____

23 Write the coordinates of E → (___,___)

24 Draw a cross at (−4, −2).

Mark the test. Remember to fill in your score on page 3.

Write your score out of 24. ⬚

Add a bonus point if you scored 20 or more.

TOTAL SCORE FOR TEST 3 ⬚

Get started

Percentages are hundredths, or numbers out of 100.

Example: In a spelling test you score 18 out of 20. $\frac{18}{20} = \frac{90}{100} = 90\%$

Example: What is 20% of £80?

With this type of question the word 'of' means multiply. There are several ways to work out percentages of amounts:

Method 1

Change to a fraction and work it out:

$\frac{20}{100} \times £80 = \frac{1600}{100} = £16$

Method 2

Use 10% to work it out – just divide by 10: 10% of £80 is £8.

So, 20% of £80 is double that: £16

To find 5%, calculate half of 10%.

Practice

1 Change these test scores to percentages.

a   8 out of 10 = _____   b 14 out of 20 = _____   c 10 out of 25 = _____

d 42 out of 50 = _____   e 17 out of 20 = _____   f 19 out of 25 = _____

g   4 out of 20 = _____   h 24 out of 25 = _____   i 28 out of 50 = _____

j   6 out of 25 = _____   k   2 out of 10 = _____   l 19 out of 20 = _____

2 Write these as percentages.

a $\frac{3}{10} \rightarrow$ _____   b $\frac{9}{10} \rightarrow$ _____   c $\frac{89}{100} \rightarrow$ _____   d $\frac{1}{4} \rightarrow$ _____

e $\frac{3}{4} \rightarrow$ _____   f $\frac{1}{5} \rightarrow$ _____   g $\frac{2}{5} \rightarrow$ _____   h $\frac{4}{5} \rightarrow$ _____

i $\frac{11}{25} \rightarrow$ _____   j $\frac{17}{20} \rightarrow$ _____   k $\frac{19}{25} \rightarrow$ _____   l $\frac{49}{50} \rightarrow$ _____

3 Complete each fraction.

a 50% = $\frac{\Box}{2}$ b 20% = $\frac{\Box}{5}$ c 90% = $\frac{\Box}{10}$ d 15% = $\frac{\Box}{20}$

e 62% = $\frac{\Box}{50}$ f 75% = $\frac{\Box}{4}$ g 45% = $\frac{\Box}{20}$ h 74% = $\frac{\Box}{50}$

Challenge

4 Find 10% of the following amounts.

a £3.40→ ☐ b £1.90→ ☐ c £4.60→ ☐ d £12→ ☐ e £28→ ☐

f £48→ ☐ g £61→ ☐ h £52.50→ ☐ i £32.80→ ☐ j £19.70→ ☐

5 Find 20% of the following amounts.

a £1.80→ ☐ b £3.60→ ☐ c £5.20→ ☐ d £14→ ☐ e £23→ ☐

f £58→ ☐ g £39→ ☐ h £32.90→ ☐ i £18.60→ ☐ j £23.10→ ☐

6 Find 5% of the following amounts.

a £6.80→ ☐ b £4.20→ ☐ c £1.60→ ☐ d £18→ ☐ e £24→ ☐

f £15→ ☐ g £31→ ☐ h £12.80→ ☐ i £23.40→ ☐ j £32.20→ ☐

7 All these items are sale bargains.
Calculate the reduced price of each.

a

£48
SALE
25% off

b

£23
SALE
50% off

c

£25.50
SALE
10% off

d

£20
SALE
40% off

e

£12.50
SALE
20% off

f

£5.20
SALE
5% off

Teacher's tips

To quickly find a percentage, divide by 100 (you can position a decimal point in the number to do this quickly) then multiply by the percentage required.

Topic 20: Special numbers

Get started

- **Multiples** are numbers made by multiplying together two other numbers.

  Multiples of 6 are 6, 12, 18, 24... **Multiples of 7** are 7, 14, 21, 28...

  Multiples go on and on. They do not stop at the tenth multiple.

- **Factors** are numbers that divide exactly into a number. It is useful to put them in pairs. **Factors of 18** in pairs are (1,18) (2, 9) (3, 6).

  Numbers that only have two factors are called **prime numbers**.

  The **factors of 17** are (1,17) so 17 is a prime number.

- **Square numbers** are made by multiplying two identical whole numbers.
  $3 \times 3 = 9$ so 9 is a **square number**; or $3 \times 3 = 3^2$ so $3^2 = 9$

- **Square roots** are the opposite of square numbers. To find the square root of 25, find a number which multiplies by itself to make 25: $\sqrt{25} = 5$

Practice

1 Circle the odd one out in each set.

a Multiples of 2
3208, 4164, 2600,
3045, 6802

b Multiples of 3
4185, 6003, 2836,
5031, 2934

c Multiples of 4
4196, 3752, 9104,
4254, 1928

d Multiples of 5
2305, 6610, 3452,
5065, 9300

e Multiples of 6
3840, 6124, 4338,
5082, 3102

f Multiples of 9
1494, 3780, 9218,
4635, 1503

2 Write all the pairs of factors of each of these numbers.

a   15   b   21   c   20   d   45   e   24   f   40
(__, __)   (__, __)   (__, __)   (__, __)   (__, __)   (__, __)
(__, __)   (__, __)   (__, __)   (__, __)   (__, __)   (__, __)
                      (__, __)   (__, __)   (__, __)   (__, __)
                                            (__, __)   (__, __)

3 Complete these.

a $4^2 = \underline{}$ b $8^2 = \underline{}$ c $7^2 = \underline{}$ d $11^2 = \underline{}$ e $15^2 = \underline{}$ f $20^2 = \underline{}$

g $\sqrt{36} = \underline{}$ h $\sqrt{4} = \underline{}$ i $\sqrt{100} = \underline{}$ j $\sqrt{25} = \underline{}$ k $\sqrt{81} = \underline{}$ l $\sqrt{144} = \underline{}$

Challenge

4 Answer these questions about this set of numbers.

13　　**45**　　**18**　　**36**　　**21**

a Which number is a prime number? _____

b Which two numbers are factors of 90? _____ and _____

c Which number is a square number? _____

d Which two numbers are multiples of both 6 and 9? _____ and _____

e Which number is the square root of 169? _____

f Which number has four factors? _____

5 These sequences are consecutive prime numbers.
Write the missing units digits.

a | 7　　11　　1◯　　1◯　　1◯　　2◯

b | 29　　3◯　　3◯　　4◯　　4◯　　4◯

c | 59　　6◯　　6◯　　7◯　　7◯　　7◯

d | 83　　8◯　　9◯　　10◯　　10◯　　10◯

6 Write these numbers in the correct part of the Venn diagram.

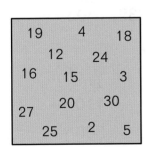

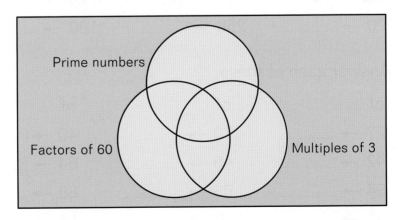

Factors of 60　　Prime numbers　　Multiples of 3

Teacher's tips

Prime numbers only have 2 factors (and one is 1). Learn the squares of numbers to 12 and you'll be able to recognise square roots. Be careful with the notation for squared, e.g. 3 squared is written 3^2.

Topic 21: Fractions of numbers

Get started

Fractions have a **numerator** and a **denominator**.

$\dfrac{2}{3}$ ← **numerator**

← **denominator**

What is $\frac{1}{5}$ of 60?

When the numerator is 1, you simply divide by the denominator.

$\frac{1}{5}$ of 60 = 60 ÷ 5 = 12

What is $\frac{3}{5}$ of 60?

When the numerator is more than 1, you divide by the denominator then multiply by the numerator.

$\frac{1}{5}$ of 60 = 12

$\frac{3}{5}$ of 60 = 12 × 3 = 36

Practice

1 Answer each of these.

a $\frac{1}{3}$ of …	b $\frac{1}{5}$ of …	c $\frac{1}{4}$ of …	d $\frac{1}{10}$ of …
24 → _____	80 → _____	60 → _____	300 → _____
51 → _____	95 → _____	84 → _____	120 → _____
99 → _____	65 → _____	96 → _____	250 → _____
72 → _____	110 → _____	124 → _____	600 → _____
120 → _____	250 → _____	180 → _____	1000 → _____

2 Answer each of these.

a $\frac{2}{3}$ of …	b $\frac{4}{5}$ of …	c $\frac{3}{4}$ of …	d $\frac{7}{10}$ of …
27 → _____	70 → _____	40 → _____	110 → _____
42 → _____	45 → _____	64 → _____	300 → _____
54 → _____	95 → _____	88 → _____	50 → _____
81 → _____	120 → _____	112 → _____	500 → _____
150 → _____	200 → _____	136 → _____	800 → _____

Challenge

3 Calculate these amounts.

a $\frac{3}{5}$ of £75 _____   b $\frac{2}{3}$ of £24 _____   c $\frac{3}{10}$ of £130 _____   d $\frac{5}{6}$ of £36 _____

e $\frac{3}{8}$ of £32 _____   f $\frac{3}{4}$ of £120 _____   g $\frac{7}{12}$ of £36 _____   h $\frac{2}{5}$ of £100 _____

4 Write the missing numbers.

a $\frac{1}{2}$ of ☐ = 18   b $\frac{1}{8}$ of ☐ = 8   c $\frac{2}{3}$ of ☐ = 10   d $\frac{3}{10}$ of ☐ = 60

e $\frac{5}{8}$ of ☐ = 40   f $\frac{3}{4}$ of ☐ = 12   g $\frac{4}{5}$ of ☐ = 24   h $\frac{7}{10}$ of ☐ = 35

5 Circle the heavier mass.

a $\frac{1}{2}$ of 3 kg or $\frac{1}{4}$ of 5 kg   b $\frac{7}{10}$ of 4 kg or $\frac{2}{3}$ of 3600 g

c $\frac{3}{5}$ of 8 kg or $\frac{3}{4}$ of 6 kg   d $\frac{2}{3}$ of 1500 g or $\frac{3}{4}$ of 1600 g

e $\frac{1}{4}$ of 3.2 kg or $\frac{1}{5}$ of 3.5 kg   f $\frac{4}{5}$ of 10 kg or $\frac{7}{10}$ of 12 kg

6 Answer these. Cancel to the lowest fraction.

a What fraction of 1 kilogram is:

a) 600 g ⟶ _____   b) 250 g ⟶ _____

c) 450 g ⟶ _____   d) 400 g ⟶ _____

e) 500 g ⟶ _____   f) 125 g ⟶ _____

b What fraction of 1 litre is:

a) 700 ml ⟶ _____   b) 300 ml ⟶ _____

c) 100 ml ⟶ _____   d) 625 ml ⟶ _____

e) 750 ml ⟶ _____

c What fraction of 1 kilometre is:

a) 250 m ⟶ _____   b) 875 m ⟶ _____

c) 900 m ⟶ _____   d) 450 m ⟶ _____

e) 200 m ⟶ _____

Teacher's tips

Follow this simple rule to find a fraction of a number: **d**ivide by the **d**enominator then times by the **n**umber of the **n**umerator.

Topic 22: Averages

Get started

There are three types of average.

What is the average of this set of numbers? **7 5 3 8 6 3 3**

Mode	Median	Mean
The mode of a set of data is the value that occurs the most often.	The median is the middle number.	This is what we normally think of as average.

Mode

The mode of a set of data is the value that occurs the most often.

The mode for this set of numbers is 3.

Median

The median is the middle number.

To work out the median:

- Put the numbers in order

  3, 3, 3, 5, 6, 7, 8

- Find the middle

  3, 3, 3, **5**, 6, 7, 8

The median is 5.

Mean

This is what we normally think of as average.

$$\text{mean} = \frac{\text{total}}{\text{number of items}}$$

$7 + 5 + 3 + 8 + 6 + 3 + 3 = 35$

There are 7 numbers.

$35 \div 7 = 5$

The mean is 5.

Practice

1 Find the median and mode for the following data:

a

Name	Jo	Lee	Scott	Rory	Sarah	Ali	Maria
Number of siblings	1	2	2	3	1	0	1

Median ⟶ _____   Mode ⟶ _____

b

Class	1	2	3	4	5	6	7
Number of siblings	27	26	31	33	30	29	31

Median ⟶ _____   Mode ⟶ _____

c Time taken to run 200 m

Name	Sam	Mark	Ashley	David	Ross
Time	34 secs	29 secs	31 secs	28 secs	31 secs

Median ⟶ _____   Mode ⟶ _____

Challenge

2 Find the mean of each set of numbers.

a 86, 98, 125, 163 ☐

b 176, 246, 433 ☐

c 92, 87, 138, 144, 164 ☐

d 199, 237, 368, 140 ☐

e 57, 46, 52, 34, 66 ☐

f 36, 25, 44, 37, 21, 17 ☐

3 This table shows the results of a maths test for a group of children. The scores are out of 100.

82	76	83	92	76	82	63	71	90	89	76

a Write the scores in order, starting with the lowest.

b Which score is the mode? _____
c Which is the median score? _____
d Calculate the mean of the scores. _____

4 These are the heights and weights of four people.

Name	Height	Weight
Joanne	1.36 m	30 kg
Kathy	1.25 m	34 kg
Jack	1.5 m	40 kg
Khuram	1.45 m	32 kg

a What is their mean height? _____

b What is their mean weight? _____

c Who is below the average weight? _____

d Who is above the average height? _____

Teacher's tips

List the numbers in order. To find the median cross off the two 'outer' numbers (highest and lowest) until you have one left. When there are two numbers left the median is the average of those two numbers.

Get started

When you add or subtract money, make sure the columns are in line.	When you calculate with pounds and pence, it is sometimes easier to change it all to pence.

The decimal points should be underneath each other.

$$\begin{array}{r} {}^{1}\ {}^{13}\quad{}^{1}\\ \pounds 2 \cancel{4} . 6\ 8 \\ -\pounds\ \ 9 . 7\ 5 \\ \hline \pounds 1\ 4 . 9\ 3 \end{array}$$

£5.84 ÷ 4
584p ÷ 4 = 146p
146p = £1.46

Practice

1 Write the change from £50 for each of these.

a £12.76 and £15.47   Change ____   b £18.05 and £12.46   Change ____

c £14.66 and £8.73   Change ____   d £7.86 and £33.29   Change ____

e £16.28 and £21.96   Change ____   f £10.85 and £32.96   Change ____

2 These are the prices of some tickets.

Theatre	Cinema	Ice hockey	Disco	Swimming
£12.45	£3.90	£8.55	£3.49	£2.54

Calculate the cost of the following: a 5 cinema tickets → _____

b 6 ice hockey tickets → _____   c 8 swimming tickets → _____

d 3 theatre tickets → _____   e 9 disco tickets → _____

3 Answer these.

a If six T-shirts cost a total of £27.36, what will one T-shirt cost? _____

b If eight videos cost £27.92, what will two videos cost? _____

c If four glasses cost £14.24, what will six glasses cost? _____

d If three CDs cost £25.47, what will five CDs cost? _____

Challenge

4 The Lewis family (2 adults and 2 children) are thinking about buying a family membership ticket for their local leisure club.

> ## LEISURE CLUB
> Daily admission prices
> Adults: £3.50   Children: £1.25
>
> Annual family membership ticket
> (2 adults, 2 children): £940

a What is the total daily cost for the whole family? _____

b If they visited as a family twice a week for four weeks, how much would it cost them in total for daily admissions? _____

c How many times would the Lewis family need to visit the leisure club in a year for their membership ticket to be cheaper than paying at each visit?
_____.

5 Circle the pack that is the better value of each pair.

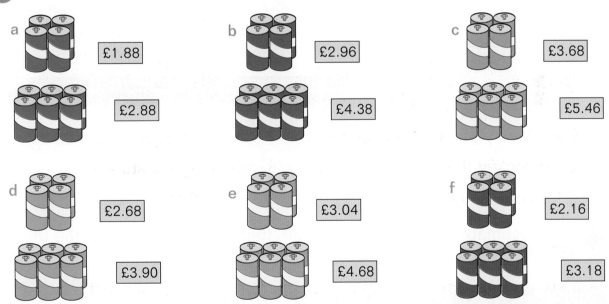

a £1.88

£2.88

b £2.96

£4.38

c £3.68

£5.46

d £2.68

£3.90

e £3.04

£4.68

f £2.16

£3.18

Teacher's tips

Convert all the values to pence before you start. For pounds and pence (e.g. £2.25) a quick way to do this is to simply remove the decimal point (225p). Make sure you use the correct notation (£ or p) in your answer.

Get started

An **angle** is a measure of turn between two lines. Angles are measured in degrees (°).

These are special angles to remember:

360° (full circle)   180° (straight line)   90° (right angle)

Acute angle (less than a right angle)   **Obtuse** angle (between 90° and 180°)   **Reflex** angle (between 180° and 360°)

All the angles of a triangle add up to 180°

$a + b + c = 180°$

All the angles of a quadrilateral add up to 360°

$a + b + c + d = 360°$

Practice

1 Write the letter for each angle in the table, under the correct heading.

Acute angles	Obtuse angles	Right angles

2 Now estimate the size of each angle, then measure and fill in the table.

Angle	a	b	c	d	e	f	g	h	i	j	k	l
Estimated size (°)												
Measured size (°)												

3 Write the missing angle on each of these triangles.

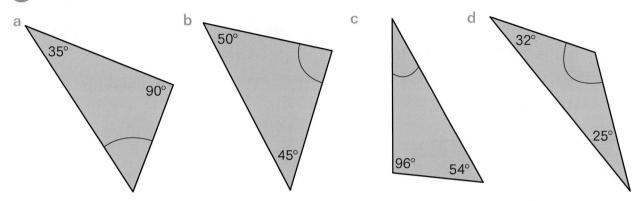

4 Write the missing angle on each of these quadrilaterals.

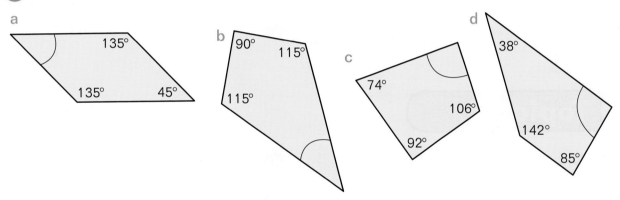

5 Calculate the missing angles.

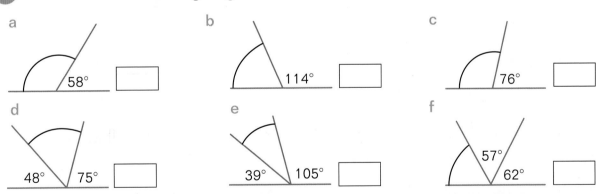

Teacher's tips

A way to remember the names of angles is that they are in alphabetical order: **A**cute (0–90 degrees), **O**btuse (90–180) and **R**eflex (180–360).

Topic 19

1 What is $\frac{4}{5}$ as a percentage? _____

2 What is 10% of £6.40? _____

3 In a test Anna scored 17 out of 20. What is this as a percentage? _____

4 A pair of shoes costing £42 is reduced by 20%.
What is the reduced price? _____

Topic 20

5 Circle the multiple of both 4 and 6.
32 56 72 42

6 Write the factors of 42.
(__, __) (__, __) (__, __) (__, __)

7 What is 7^2? _____

8 The square root of 121 is _____

Topic 21

9 What is one-fifth of 400? _____

10 $\frac{3}{8}$ of £40 = _____

11 Write the missing number.
$\frac{3}{4}$ of ☐ = 24

12 What fraction of 1 kilogram is 925 g? _____

Topic 22

Look at this set of numbers.
14, 8, 11, 9, 14, 8, 15, 6, 14

14 What is the mean? _____

13 What is the mode? _____

15 What is the median? _____

16 21 is added to make this a set of ten numbers. What is the mean now? _____

Topic 23

17 A football costs £13.79. What is the change from £20? _____

18 What change would you get from £5 for a sandwich at £1.68 and two cakes at 68p each? _____

19 Tickets to a football match cost £23.15 each. What is the total cost for eight tickets? _____

20 If five plants cost a total of £15.45, what would three plants cost? _____

Topic 24

21 Circle the acute angle.

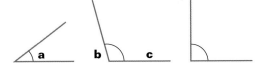

22 Tick the angle that shows 45°.

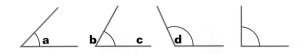

23 What is the missing angle?

_____

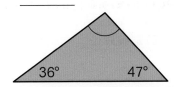

24 What is the missing angle?

_____

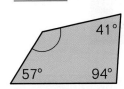

Mark the test. Now add up all your test scores and put your final score on page 3.

Write your score out of 24.

Add a bonus point if you scored 20 or more.

TOTAL SCORE FOR TEST 4

Answers

Topic 1: Place value – decimals (page 4)

1.
a. 0.6	**b.** 0.04		
c. 2	**d.** 0.005		
e. 0.1	**f.** 0.09		
g. 0.07	**h.** 0.008		
i. 0.6	**j.** 0.009		

2.
a. 0.4	**b.** 0.7	**c.** 0.5	**d.** 0.3
e. 0.9	**f.** 0.45	**g.** 0.64	**h.** 0.92
i. 0.08	**j.** 0.14	**k.** 0.755	**l.** 0.25
m. 0.399	**n.** 0.925	**o.** 0.078	

3.
a. 72	**b.** 615	**c.** 1.21	**d.** 0.146
163	380	1.48	0.3
4.5	277	0.76	0.893
10.33	5.1	0.035	0.065
8.05	120.3	0.901	0.008

4.
a. 0.02	0.05	0.06	0.08
b. 0.03	0.08	0.14	0.17
c. 0.001	0.003	0.006	0.009
d. 0.004	0.009	0.016	0.018

5.
a. 1.028
b. 0.532
c. 0.963
d. 1.158

Topic 2: Mental addition (page 6)

1.
a. 220	**b.** 119	**c.** 17.3	**d.** 285
310	119	8.7	11.5
530	106	18.3	4100
430	77	13.5	18.3
560	101	11.6	325
640	105	15	12.21
530	107	9.4	1680
440	121	18.8	14.65
920	143	11.3	6022
830	102	17.2	0.71

2.
a. 53	**b.** 710	**c.** 0.44
62	540	0.77
44	630	0.81
52.5	415	0.63
35.5	395	0.95
16.5	725	0.88

3.

a.
6.3	2.7	**9**
8.8	0.1	**8.9**
15.1	**2.8**	**17.9**

b.
7.1	0.4	**7.5**
8.2	4.9	**13.1**
15.3	**5.3**	**20.6**

c.
2.3	1.9	**4.2**
0.7	2.5	**3.2**
3	**4.4**	**7.4**

d.
6.4	8.7	**15.1**
2.9	5.6	**8.5**
9.3	**14.3**	**23.6**

4.
a. 27	28	29
b. 39	40	41
c. 74	75	76
d. 219	220	221
e. 53	54	55
f. 97	98	99

Topic 3: Mental subtraction (page 8)

1.
a. 50	**b.** 45	**c.** 6.3	**d.** 187
170	21	10.9	2.6
370	23	7.9	1400
280	56	7.9	8.3
380	39	8.4	187
470	56	15.8	5.31

2.
a. 24	**b.** 20
c. 270	**d.** 197
e. 0.11	**f.** 0.07
g. 86	**h.** 96
i. 640	**j.** 810
k. 0.63	**l.** 0.65

3.
a. 3.8	**b.** 1.8
4.5	5.5
4.5	7.7
3.6	12.5
3.5	12.4
c. 3500	**d.** 8
3300	11
4700	33
3600	39
2900	15

4.
a. 1.4	**b.** 5.2
2.8	7.5
3.9	3.8
0.7	8.6
9.5	2.7
8.9	6.9

5.
a. 351	111	
b. 302	3	2.02
c. 428	230	43
d. 133	33.5	13.7

Topic 4: Area and perimeter (page 10)

1.
a. 63 cm²	**b.** 28 cm²
32 cm	23 cm
c. 2700 mm²	**d.** 360cm²
210 mm	76 cm

2.
a. 60 cm²	**b.** 72 m²
38 cm	40 m
c. 98 cm²	**d.** 123 m²
48 cm	54 m

3.
a. 25 cm²	**b.** 18 cm²
c. 64 cm²	**d.** 70 cm²
e. 72 cm²	**f.** 216 cm²
g. 140 cm²	**h.** 28 cm²

4.
Area of whole garden:	714 m²
Area of paving:	314 m²
Area of lawn:	355 m²
Area of pond:	45 m²

Topic 5: Multiplication and division (page 12)

1.
a. 45	**b.** 66	**c.** 7	**d.** 11
42	49	7	6
64	60	7	12
27	32	7	9
40	77	7	12
36	56	7	12
81	72	8	6
63	72	9	11
48	110	8	12
	108	6	9

2.
a. 25	**b.** 64
c. 81	**d.** 36
e. 49	**f.** 100
g. 144	**h.** 400
i. 121	**j.** 900

3.
a. 3	**b.** 16
c. 0.9	**d.** 7.5
e. 1	**f.** 11
g. 0.5	**h.** 0.2
i. 11	**j.** 9
k. 0.32	**l.** 4500
m. 4.2	**n.** 43
o. 6.5	

4.
a.
IN	47	**57**	0.16	**340**	4800	**4.25**	12.7	**40.5**
OUT	**94**	114	**0.32**	680	**9600**	8.5	**25.4**	81

b.
IN	0.9	**344**	570	**1.7**	6500	**218**	17.8	**0.14**
OUT	**0.45**	172	**285**	0.85	**3250**	109	**8.9**	0.07

5.
a.
x	7	9	6
5	35	**45**	30
9	**63**	**81**	**54**
8	**56**	**72**	48

b.
x	0.4	0.9	0.3
6	**2.4**	**5.4**	**1.8**
7	**2.8**	**6.3**	**2.1**
5	**2**	**4.5**	**1.5**

c.
x	**1.3**	1.4	1.9
6	**7.8**	**8.4**	**11.4**
8	**10.4**	11.2	**15.2**
4	5.2	**5.6**	**7.6**

d.
x	0.5	0.7	**0.6**
0.8	**0.4**	0.56	**0.48**
0.4	0.2	**0.28**	**0.24**
0.3	**0.15**	**0.21**	0.18

Topic 6: 2D shapes (page 14)

1.
Shape	A	B	C	D	E	F	G	H
Square							✓	
Rhombus			✓	✓				
Rectangle				✓		✓	✓	
Parallelogram	✓		✓	✓		✓	✓	✓
Trapezium					✓			
Kite		✓						

2.
a. Odd one out: kite (E)	All others: rhombuses
b. Odd one out: trapezium (D)	All others: rectangles
c. Odd one out: rhombus (D)	All others: kites
d. Odd one out: trapezium (B)	All others: parallelograms
e. Odd one out: kite (D)	All others: squares
f. Odd one out: kite (F)	All others: trapeziums

3.

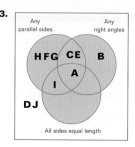

Test 1 (page 16)

1. 0.003 or $\frac{3}{1000}$
2. 0.35   0.285
3. 59   0.082
4. 0.03   0.07
5. 820
6. 0.93
7. 15.8
8. 54
9. 58
10. 2.55
11. 15
12. 7.5
13. 37.5 cm²
14. 25 cm²
15. 22 m²

16. 22 m
17. 72   132
18. 4
19. 2.4
20. 81
21. trapeziums; C has a right angle
22. parallelogram and quadrilateral
23. C
24.

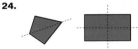

Topic 7: Time (page 18)

1.
a. 08:25
b. 16:35
c. 19:55
d. 10:05
e. 21:53
f. 02:17
g. 11:28
h. 22:34
i. 01:23
j. 20:59
k. 09:14
l. 23:42

2.
a. 6.35 am
b. 1.45 pm
c. 7.10 pm
d. 8.05 am
e. 12.38 pm
f. 10.41 am
g. 3.52 pm
h. 9.13 pm
i. 1.11 am
j. 11.46 pm
k. 11.19 am
l. 10.53 pm

3.

4.
02:15   3.17 am   6.50 am   09:45   12.41 pm   15:28   4.56 pm   19:13
21:06   9.10 pm

5.

Moss Lane	08:45	11:22	**16:22**	**21:11**
Brook Street	09:03	**11:40**	16:40	**21:29**
Church Road	**09:21**	11:58	**16:58**	**21:47**
Beck Avenue	**09:39**	**12:16**	**17:16**	22:05

6.
a. 20 minutes
b. 60 minutes
c. 100 minutes
d. 80 minutes
e. 155 minutes
f. 230 minutes

Topic 8: Fractions (page 20)

1.
a. $\frac{11}{5}$ b. $\frac{19}{4}$
c. $\frac{17}{10}$ d. $\frac{19}{3}$
e. $\frac{19}{8}$ f. $\frac{19}{5}$
g. $\frac{10}{7}$ h. $\frac{61}{10}$
i. $\frac{55}{12}$ j. $\frac{17}{6}$
k. $\frac{29}{3}$ l. $\frac{37}{8}$

2.
a. $4\frac{3}{4}$ b. $7\frac{1}{3}$
c. $1\frac{1}{5}$ d. $1\frac{3}{4}$
e. $3\frac{4}{5}$ f. $2\frac{7}{8}$
g. $1\frac{4}{7}$ h. $5\frac{3}{5}$
i. $5\frac{5}{7}$ j. $7\frac{4}{7}$
k. $8\frac{7}{10}$ l. $5\frac{1}{8}$

3.
a. $\frac{3}{5}$ b. $\frac{1}{2}$
c. $\frac{1}{3}$ d. $\frac{16}{25}$
e. $\frac{3}{8}$ f. $\frac{3}{4}$
g. $\frac{7}{13}$ h. $\frac{9}{10}$
i. $\frac{3}{19}$ j. $\frac{1}{5}$

4.
a. 6   25 b. 6 18
c. 6   20 d. 15 40
e. 9 100 f. 14 24
g. 10 200 h. 15 48
i. 9 70 j. 10 50
k. 15 56 l. 21 60

5.
a. $\frac{1}{4}$ $\frac{3}{8}$ $\frac{7}{12}$
b. $\frac{1}{2}$ $\frac{5}{3}$ $\frac{3}{3}$
c. $\frac{1}{12}$ $\frac{1}{3}$ $\frac{5}{6}$

Topic 9: Written addition (page 22)

1.
a. 9625
b. 15 020
c. 9563
d. 15 468
e. 13 803
f. 49 803
g. 94 078
h. 49 869
i. 61 510
j. 30 479

2.
a. £8633.30
b. £7434.93
c. £15 511.45
d. £556.78
e. £9596.35
f. £15 033.00
g. £18 081.95
h. £16 474.50
i. £17 603.50

3.
a. 95 206
b. 99 999
c. 95 206

4.
a.
```
  6 3 4 5
+ 7 4 1 5
1 3 7 6 0
```
b.
```
  4 2 7 7
+ 8 3 4 5
1 2 6 2 2
```
c.
```
  5 3 2 8
+ 5 9 7 4
1 1 3 0 2
```
d.
```
  3 8 4 7
+ 7 6 5 3
1 1 5 0 0
```
e.
```
  1 3 9 2 9
+ 4 4 6 5 3
  5 8 5 8 2
```

5.
a. 420 and 840
b. 11 110   11 111   11 112
c. 75 and 85
d. 70 and 20

Topic 10: Written subtraction (page 24)

1.
a. 2263 b. 3112
c. 2675 d. 4948
e. 449 f. 36 050
g. 11 250 h. 37 939
i. 21 864 j. 17 643

2.
a. 198.08 kg b. 962.57 kg
c. 15.53 kg d. 467.15 kg
e. 101.975 kg f. 569.125 kg

3.
a. 42 508
b. 636
c. 1651
d. 81 453 and 48 120

4.
a.
```
  8 1 7 5
- 3 0 6 9
  5 1 0 6
```
b.
```
1 0 4 7 2
-   8 5 6 5
  1 9 0 7
```
c.
```
2 4 3 6 2
-   7 6 7 8
1 6 6 8 4
```
d.
```
3 5 0 0 4
- 1 4 6 8 5
2 0 3 1 9
```
e.
```
4 2 1 2 5
- 1 8 6 9 6
2 3 4 2 9
```

5.
a. 110 and 290
b. 35 and 20
c. 350 and 610
d. 60 and 90

Topic 11: Sequences and patterns (page 26)

1.
a. 49 64 79
b. 56 45 34
c. 76 95 114
d. 18 10 2
e. 50 25 0
f. 79 72 65
g. 21 15 9
h. 84 105 126
i. 50 35 20
j. 825 800 775

2.
a. 8   32   44
b. −19 5   11
c. −30 −15 15
d. 10 21   43
e. −28 −19 −10
f. −45 0   15
g. −61 −43 −31
h. −12 0   36
i. −99 −80 −4
j. −40 −25 −10

3.
Check the following numbers of dots have been drawn:
a. 12 dots; 3, 6, 9, 12
b. 14 dots; 5, 8, 11, 14
c. 9 dots; 3, 5, 7, 9

4.
a. 25 36   49
b. 15 21   28
c. 8 13   21
10th numbers are
a. 100
b. 55
c. 55

5.
Check lines have been drawn in order between these numbers:
Note: the digital root for 28 is 1: $2 + 8 = 10 \rightarrow 1 + 0 = 1$
a. 3, 6, 9
b. 4, 8, 3, 7, 2, 6, 1, 5
c. 5, 1, 6, 2, 7, 3, 8, 4, 9

Topic 12: Comparing and ordering numbers (p28)

1.
a. 3.48 3.64 3.86 4.06
b. 4.46 4.78 4.87 5.49
c. 6.49 6.79 6.98 9.05
d. 2.17 2.87 7.12 7.22
e. 27.09 31.27 31.72 37.8
f. 16.78 17.86 75.11 75.89
g. 0.454 0.457 0.458 0.467
h. 2.445 3.036 3.243 3.321

2.
a. < **b.** < **c.** >
d. < **e.** > **f.** <
g. < **h.** < **i.** <

3.
a. 4.15
b. 5.65
c. 3.85
d. 10.95
e. 15.45
f. 0.245
g. 3.055
h. 4.825
i. 7.665
j. 1.295

4.
a. < < **b.** > <
c. > < **d.** < >
e. < > **f.** > <

5.
BOLT Usain	9.63
BLAKE Yohan	9.75
GATLIN Justin	9.79
GAY Tyson	9.80
BAILEY Ryan	9.88
MARTINA Churandy	9.94
THOMPSON Richard	9.98

Test 2 (page 30)

1. 22:28   09:52
2. 10.41a.m. 8.07p.m.
3. Hands drawn should show quarter to 12. The small hand should point to just before the 12 and the long hand should point to 45.
4. 15:08
5. $\frac{39}{5}$
6. $7\frac{5}{6}$
7. 15 32
8. $\frac{4}{17}$
9. 146 802
10. 1337.04
11. 13 235
12. £970.72
13. 26 508
14. 5588
15. 167.79
16.

6	0	1	3	4
− 4	6	8	2	9
1	3	3	0	5

17. 61, 72, 83
18. −7 11 20
19. 16 25 81 100; square numbers
20. 10 15 55 66; triangular numbers
21. < <
22. < >
23. 5.315
24. 5.868 5.899 8.659 56.89 58.69

Topic 13: Rounding numbers (page 32)

1.
a. 46 **b.** 28 **c.** 15
d. 31 **e.** 64 **f.** 84
g. 15 **h.** 93 **i.** 80
j. 3   **k.** 8   **l.** 10

2.
a. 7.5 **b.** 4.6 **c.** 1.5
d. 5.8 **e.** 8.2 **f.** 9.4
g. 6.9 **h.** 5.8 **i.** 0.8
j. 4.1 **k.** 3.9 **l.** 2.8

3. (these are estimates)
a. 0.1 0.4 0.7 0.9
b. 3.2 3.5 3.6 3.8
c. 0.02 0.05 0.06 0.08
d. 4.01 4.03 4.07 4.09
e. 0.002 0.004 0.007 0.008
f. 2.001 2.003 2.008 2.009

4. (these are estimates)
a. 21 **b.** 21.2
   96   97.8
   23   15.0
   44   12.1
   15   0.4
   56   15.8

Topic 14: Measures (page 34)

1.
a. 420 cm **b.** 50 mm
c. 12 000 m **d.** 85 dm
e. 40 000 g **f.** 4500 kg
g. 18 000 ml **h.** 390 cl
i. 52 dl **j.** 3800 mm
k. 700 ml **l.** 40 cl

2. (these answers are approximate)
a. 4 inches **b.** 120 g
c. 4 gallons **d.** 10 litres
e. 8 kg **f.** 5 miles

3.
a. 300 ml
b. 80 cm
c. 112 km
d. 2.25 kg
e. 3.6 kg
f. 3 litres

4.
a. 3 feet
b. 2000 mm
c. 20 miles
d. 2 feet
e. 15 m
f. 100 inches

5.
Pounds	1	2	**5**	0.5	**7.5**	10	**8.8**	8
Kilograms	0.45	**0.9**	2.25	**0.225**	3.4	**4.5**	4	**3.6**

Topic 15: 3D shapes (page 36)

1.
a. triangular prism
b. cuboid
c. cube
d. tetrahedron
e. square-based pyramid
f. hexagonal prism

2.
Cuboid	→ 4 rectangular faces and 2 square faces
Cube	→ 6 square faces
Tetrahedron	→ 4 triangular faces
Triangular prism	→ 2 triangular faces and 3 rectangular faces
Square-based pyramid	→ 1 square face and 4 triangular faces
Octahedron	→ 8 triangular faces
Pentagonal prism	→ 2 pentagonal faces and 5 rectangular faces
Dodecahedron	→ 12 pentagonal faces

3.
a. triangular prism
b. cuboid
c. cube
d. tetrahedron
e. square-based pyramid
f. pentagonal prism

4.
Name of shape	Number of faces	Number of edges	Number of vertices
Cuboid	6	12	8
Tetrahedron	4	6	4
Square-based pyramid	5	8	5
Pentagonal prism	7	15	10
Triangular prism	5	9	6
Dodecahedron	12	30	20
Octahedron	8	12	6

Rule: <u>number of faces + number of vertices − 2 = number of edges</u>

Topic 16: Multiplication (page 38)

1.
a. 2000 **b.** 4800 **c.** 3500
d. 1400 **e.** 3600 **f.** 3000
g. 5400 **h.** 7200 **i.** 5600
j. 2100 **k.** 16 000 **l.** 28 000

2.
a. 3024
b. 9568

3.
a. 2688
b. 17 898
c. 45 276

4.
a. 3555
b. 5644
c. 4833
d. 1464
e. 35 322
f. 35 224

5.
a. £1020
b. 3456
c. 2444
d. 1674 g
e. £1112

6.
a. (estimate) 3000 cm²
   (actual) 3024 cm²
b. (estimate) 3600 cm²
   (actual) 3666 cm²
c. (estimate) 18 000 cm²
   (actual) 18 966 cm²
d. (estimate) 24 000 cm²
   (actual) 21 948 cm²

Topic 17: Division (page 40)

1.
a. 70 **b.** 95
c. 62 **d.** 175
e. 90 **f.** 120
g. 90 **h.** 50
i. 188 **j.** 160
k. 240 **l.** 30
m. 70 **n.** 70
o. 194

2.
a. 71 r 3 **b.** 27 r 3
c. 148 r 3 **d.** 48 r 2
e. 165 r 1 **f.** 65 r 2
g. 49 r 4 **h.** 71 r 6
i. 263 r 1 **j.** 120 r 5

3.
a. 52 weeks and 2 days
b. 187
c. 65
d. 42
e. 30
f. 83

4.
271 ÷ 6 → r 1
315 ÷ 8 → r 3
454 ÷ 5 → r 4
608 ÷ 3 → r 2
259 ÷ 9 → r 7
359 ÷ 10 → r 9
458 ÷ 9 → r 8

398 ÷ 7 → r 6
Check that your child's extra division has a remainder of 5.

5.
a. 592 ÷ 4 = 148
b. 476 ÷ 3 = 158 r 2
c. 389 ÷ 5 = 77 r 4

Topic 18: Coordinates (page 42)

1.
A → (−4, 2)   C → (2, 5)
E → (0, −1)   G → (−2, −5)
(5, −5) → B   (−5, 0) → F
(−3, −3) → D   (3, −4) → H

2.
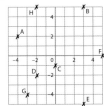

3.
Triangle 1 → isosceles
Triangle 2 → right-angled

4.
A → (−2, 4) B → (4, 0) C → (2, −3)
D → (−4, 1)
Check that D is plotted correctly and that a rectangle has been drawn.

5.
A → (−3, 3)
B → (2, 3)
Check that points C and D have been plotted correctly.
The shape is a kite.

Test 3 (page 44)

1. 16
   84
2. 1.8
   4.1
3. 3.02 3.06 3.09 (These are estimates.)
4. 83 } (These are estimates.)
   32
5. 2.55 metres
6. 4.32 kg
7. 45 litres
8. 60 miles
9. tetrahedron
10. triangular prism
11. cube
12. 5 faces, 8 edges and 5 vertices
13. 24 857
14. 28 260
15. 21 000
16. 17 536 g
17. 120
18. 63
19. 82 r 4
20. 58p
21. (−3, 5)
22. B
23. (6, 1)
24. Check that a cross has been plotted at (−4, −2).

Topic 19: Percentages (page 46)

1.
a. 80% **b.** 70%
c. 40% **d.** 84%
e. 85% **f.** 76%
g. 20% **h.** 96%
i. 56% **j.** 24%
k. 20% **l.** 95%

2.
a. 30% **b.** 90%
c. 89% **d.** 25%
e. 75% **f.** 20%
g. 40% **h.** 80%
i. 44% **j.** 85%
k. 76% **l.** 98%

3.
a. 1 **b.** 1
c. 9 **d.** 3
e. 31 **f.** 3
g. 9 **h.** 37

4.
a. 34p **b.** 19p
c. 46p **d.** £1.20
e. £2.80 **f.** £4.80
g. £6.10 **h.** £5.25
i. £3.28 **j.** £1.97

5.
a. 36p **b.** 72p
c. £1.04 **d.** £2.80
e. £4.60 **f.** £11.60
g. £7.80 **h.** £6.58
i. £3.72 **j.** £4.62

6.
a. 34p **b.** 21p
c. 8p **d.** 90p
e. £1.20 **f.** 75p
g. £1.55 **h.** 64p
i. £1.17 **j.** £1.61

7.
a. £36
b. £11.50
c. £22.95
d. £12
e. £10
f. £4.94

Topic 20: Special numbers (page 48)

1.
a. 3045
b. 2836
c. 4254
d. 3452
e. 6124
f. 9218

2.
a. (1, 15) (3, 5)
b. (1, 21) (3, 7)
c. (1, 20) (2, 10) (4, 5)
d. (1, 45) (3, 15) (5, 9)
e. (1, 24) (2, 12) (3, 8)   (4, 6)
f. (1, 40) (2, 20) (4, 10) (5, 8)

3.
a. 16 **g.** 6
b. 64 **h.** 2
c. 49 **i.** 10
d. 121 **j.** 5
e. 225 **k.** 9
f. 400 **l.** 12

4.
a. 13
b. 45 and 18
c. 36
d. 18 and 36
e. 13
f. 21

5.
a. 3 7 9 3
b. 1 7 1 3 7
c. 1 7 1 3 9
d. 9 7 1 3 7

6.
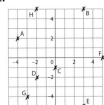

Topic 21: Fractions of numbers (page 50)

1.
a. 8 **b.** 16
   17   19
   33   13
   24   22
   40   50
c. 15 **d.** 30
   21   12
   24   25
   31   60
   45   100

2.
a. 18 **b.** 56
   28   36
   36   76
   54   96
   100   160
c. 30 **d.** 77
   48   210
   66   35
   84   350
   102   560

3.
a. £45
b. £16
c. £39
d. £30
e. £12
f. £90
g. £21
h. £40

4.
a. 36
b. 64
c. 15
d. 200
e. 64
f. 16
g. 30
h. 50

5.
a. $\frac{1}{2}$ of 3 kg
b. $\frac{7}{10}$ of 4 kg
c. $\frac{3}{5}$ of 8 kg
d. $\frac{3}{4}$ of 1600 g
e. $\frac{1}{4}$ of 3.2 kg
f. $\frac{7}{10}$ of 12 kg

6.
a. a) $\frac{3}{5}$ **b.** a) $\frac{7}{10}$ **c.** a) $\frac{1}{4}$
   b) $\frac{1}{4}$ b) $\frac{3}{10}$ b) $\frac{7}{8}$
   c) $\frac{9}{20}$ c) $\frac{1}{10}$ c) $\frac{9}{10}$
   d) $\frac{2}{5}$ d) $\frac{5}{8}$ d) $\frac{9}{20}$
   e) $\frac{1}{2}$ e) $\frac{3}{4}$ e) $\frac{1}{5}$
   f) $\frac{1}{8}$

Topic 22: Averages (page 52)

1.
a. Median →1   Mode → 1
b. Median → 30   Mode → 31
c. Median → 31 seconds   Mode → 31 seconds

2.
a. 118
b. 285
c. 125
d. 236
e. 51
f. 30

3.
a. 63 71 76 76 76 82 82 83 89 90 92
b. 76
c. 82
d. 80

4.
a. 1.39 m
b. 34 kg
c. Joanne and Khuram
d. Jack and Khuram

Topic 23: Money (page 54)

1.
a. £21.77
b. £19.49
c. £26.61
d. £8.85
e. £11.76
f. £6.19

2.
a. £19.50
b. £51.30
c. £20.32
d. £37.35
e. £31.41

3.
a. £4.56
b. £6.98
c. £21.36
d. £42.45

4.
a. £9.50
b. £76
c. 99 visits

5.
a. 4 cans for £1.88
b. 6 cans for £4.38
c. 6 cans for £5.46
d. 6 cans for £3.90
e. 4 cans for £3.04
f. 6 cans for £3.18

Topic 24: Angles (page 56)

1.

Acute angles	Obtuse angles	Right angles
a e	c d	b
g i	f j	h
k	l	

2.

Angle	a	b	c	d	e	f	g	h	i	j	k	l
Estimated size ( )	Check that estimates are within 5° either side of the measured size.											
Measured size ( )	60	90	140	125	45	110	20	90	30	160	80	100

3.
a. 55°
b. 85°
c. 30°
d. 123°

4.
a. 45°
b. 40°
c. 88°
d. 95°

5.
a. 122°
b. 66°
c. 104°
d. 57°
e. 36°
f. 61°

Test 4 (page 58)

1. 80%
2. 64p
3. 85%
4. £33.60
5. 72
6. (1, 42) (2, 21) (3, 14) (6, 7)
7. 49
8. 11
9. 80
10. £15
11. 32
12. $\frac{37}{40}$
13. 14
14. 11
15. 11
16. 12
17. £6.21
18. £1.96
19. £185.20
20. £9.27
21. angle a
22. angle a
23. 97°
24. 168°